The
Chemicals
We Eat

BOOKS BY MELVIN A. BENARDE:

Race Against Famine (1968)

Our Precarious Habitat (1970)

Disinfection (1970)

The Chemicals We Eat

by DR. MELVIN A. BENARDE

*The destiny of nations depends upon
the manner in which they are fed*

BRILLAT-SAVARIN
PHYSIOLOGIE DU GOÛT, 1825

McGraw-Hill Book Company

New York • St. Louis • San Francisco • London • Paris • Düsseldorf
Tokyo • Kuala Lumpur • Mexico • Montreal • Panama • São Paulo
Sydney • Toronto • Johannesburg • New Delhi • Singapore

Library of Congress Catalog Card Number: 79-142976
0-07-004424-4

First McGraw-Hill Paperback Edition, 1975

1234567890   MUMU   798765

To Anita, for so much—

CONTENTS

FIGURES AND TABLES

TABLES

The
Chemicals
We Eat

Introduction to the Paperback Edition

If one word or idea could be said to characterize the temper of the times vis à vis chemicals in foods, it would have to be safety. And rightly so. A public dependent upon a vast industry for its food ought not to have to worry about the safety of the supply; it should be taken for granted.

Since the initial appearance of *The Chemicals We Eat,* a number of significant developments have convincingly demonstrated that uncompromising safety of our food supply is an attainable goal.

During the past four years, tests and testing of chemicals for carcinogenicity, mutagenicity and teratogenicity have been the shibboleth of government, industry and academia, and a word about each condition is warranted.

· **Carcinogenicity** ·

It is generally agreed that the cause of the majority of human cancers remains unknown. Nevertheless, cancer is be-

1

lieved to be multicausal in origin and probably develops in response to such stimuli as chemicals, irradiation and viruses. Additional contributing factors are the genetic makeup and activity of the immune system.

We may be exposed to potential chemical carcinogens from the food we eat, the drugs we consume, or from our external environment. Potentially carcinogenic chemicals may inadvertently enter the food supply through abuse of food during production, processing or sale and distribution, or through inclusion of chemical additives during manufacture.

The development of cancer appears to follow a period of prolonged exposure and usually not until long after exposure has stopped does it manifest itself. The long latent or induction period, together with the difficulty of establishing the human carcinogenicity of a chemical, could result in a potential carcinogen being in use for many years before its harmful nature was recognized, if at all.

Experience with laboratory animals has revealed that nearly all substances that are carcinogenic in man are also carcinogenic in one or several animal species even though the tumor site or type of resultant cancer may not be the same.

In the past ten years, but even more acutely in the last five, cancer testing in animals has reached a relatively sophisticated stage and it is quite likely that exhaustive study of chemicals in animals, with the full arsenal of tests currently available, would warn us of carcinogenicity to man. However, and this is not only the shoal on which many tests founder but an operating principle as well, the demonstration of carcinogenic activity in experimental animals does not necessarily mean that a chemical is carcinogenic to man under conditions of human use. While this is fundamental to all testing, it is also the source of much controversy. Consequently, the interpretation, evaluation and extrapolation to man of cancer studies in animals becomes an extremely difficult and onerous task. Ultimately, we must all rely on and put our trust in competent scientists who have considerable experience with cancer.

Cyclamate is a case in point. Because it speaks so impressively to the issue of continued and regular evaluation and re-evaluation of the safety of food additives by regulatory agencies both national and international, it may serve our purpose to bring the as yet unfinished story of cyclamate up to date. Earlier, I wrote, "On October 21, 1969, The Food and Drug Administration ordered all production of general purpose products containing cyclamates to cease." I went on to say that, "By the middle of June, 1970, the FDA issued a statement indicating that cyclamates might not be as hazardous as previously thought, and that they would be restudied." They have been. So much so that on March 14, 1975, Dr. Alexander M. Schmidt, Commissioner of The Food and Drug Administration could write to Dr. Frank J. Rausher, Jr., Director of The National Cancer Institute to request that a blue-ribbon committee of cancer experts be impaneled to review the findings.

Some twelve studies from laboratories around the world had found cyclamate non-cancerous. These were life-time feeding studies in which a variety of animal species were fed graded doses of the sweetener for their entire lives.

In fact, the data showed in the "opinion of the oncological community of the world that cyclamates when tested in accordance with appropriate protocols are not carcinogenic."

Nevertheless, it is imperative that the data be aired openly and by an impartial jury. Dr. Schmidt was quite correct when he stated that "a re-evaluation of this matter is important because it has become of substantial interest to the public and the congress, and is particularly of interest to diabetics who wish to have available a safe and palatable artificial sweetener."

Of similar interest is the case of Saccharin. However, after evaluating data obtained from almost three years of testing, the National Academy of Sciences has been unable to state categorically that Saccharin is or is not safe. And until it is able to do so, the FDA plans to continue in force the "freeze" imposed in 1972. This means that until the impasse is broken, Saccharin can only be available at levels used prior to the freeze.

Another additive caught in the safety tug-of-war is Aspartame. Four years ago I wrote that aspartylphenylalanine ($C_{14}H_{18}N_2O_5$) 180 times as sweet as sugar (sucrose), was being safety tested as a possible replacement for cyclamate.

Since then, it received not only a new name, Aspartame, but a clean bill of health—and lost it pending the outcome of additional evaluations currently in progress.

The July 26, 1974 issue of The Federal Register (page 27317) publicly announced that G. D. Searle & Co. of Chicago had filed a petition to have Aspartame included as a food additive safe for human consumption. It also noted that the Commissioner of Food and Drugs, after evaluating Searle's data, concluded that Aspartame was safe and should be granted food additive staus.

Although Aspartame does provide four calories per gram, its intense sweetness means that to achieve a level of sweetness equivalent to sugar, approximately $\frac{1}{180}$th the amount of sugar would be required. Consequently, its caloric contribution would be nil, or insignificant. The Commissioner restricted its use to those foods normally eaten cold (for example, chewing gum, cold instant beverage mixes, puddings and fillings, cold cereal), as Aspartame was unstable and lost its sweetness during boiling or frying. Announcement in the Federal Register was tantamount to having a new sweetener on our breakfast tables. But as the proverb has it, "There's many a slip twixt the cup and the lip." For Aspartame, that meant new findings casting doubt on its safety. That was in October, 1974.

Towards the end of May, 1975, an independent panel of experts was brought together at The Massachusetts Institute of Technology to weigh the evidence; was Aspartame safe or wasn't it. An answer in the affirmative would be reflected in the availability of an entirely new family of sweeteners for those who needed them.

· **Mutagenicity** ·

A mutation is usually defined as any heritable change in genetic material.

If the genetic functioning of the cell is altered but the capacity for cell division is unimpaired, the mutation may be transmitted to descendants. For the most part, mutations are not beneficial to their recipients.

Among the undesirable changes that may occur are congenital malformations, lowered resistance to disease, reduced life span, sterility and mental retardation. That cancer may also be the result of mutagenic agents remains a highly controversial subject. Opinions for and against are to be found within the ranks of Toxicologists and Oncologists. However, as neither side can support its opinions with hard data, opinions they must remain—for the time being.

It is generally assumed that the critical target of chemical mutagens is DNA (desoxyribosenucleic acid)—the stuff that genes are made of—the basic material of all life, and curiously enough the same whether from men, mice or microbes.

Although the molecular bases of mutations are not known, three major consequences have been identified: misrepair of broken chromosomes, failure of a pair of broken chromosomes to separate (nondysjunction) and loss of chromosome during cell division.

While there is precious little evidence at the present time to suggest that an increase in the mutation rate has occurred say, since the 1940s when food additives began to be used with increasing frequency, it is nonetheless prudent to identify and eliminate exposure to potential mutagens affecting man. A major barrier to mutagenicity testing has been the complexity of methods, length of time for testing individual chemicals, and great cost. Recently, a breakthrough has been achieved—a test that holds promise of becoming a rapid screening procedure.

Dr. Bruce N. Ames, Professor of Biochemistry at The University of California, Berkeley, developed a bacterial test that appears to reveal the ability of chemicals to damage genes.

Basically, the Ames test consists of an agar-filled petri dish that is seeded with the bacterium Salmonella typhimurium. The uniqueness of this test is that the Salmonellae will only grow in the presence of a chemical mutagen added to the agar. If the chemical is not a mutagen the organism fails to grow (negative result). On the other hand, if the chemical is a mutagen, the microbe grows luxuriantly around the drop of chemical—a positive test.

In order for these bacteria to grow in the presence of a potentially mutagenic substance, Dr. Ames has had to modify the bacteria in a number of ways. Consequently, this test system is not without detractors. For example, the test has been called into question because of its artificial nature as well as the great difficulty of extrapolating the results to man as a consequence of the evolutionary distance of bacteria from man. Nevertheless, scientists in government, industry and academia see in the test a simple, quick and economic way to single out those chemicals that should be subjected to further, more costly and time-consuming animal tests.

· **Teratogenicity** ·

Teratology is defined as the study of the effects of factors related to permanent structural or functional changes induced during the development of an embryo. Hence, a teratogenic agent is one that can produce congenital malformations. Unfortunately, the present state of knowledge limits teratogenic assessment to external, gross visceral and skeletal examination.

Fortunately that state of affairs will not last too long if research studies now in progress in several laboratories in the United States and Canada bear fruit. Because the concept is so sophisticated it deserves at least brief comment.

Basically the focus is on a quantitative procedure that employs the tremendous capability of the electron microscope to enlarge and visualize the increase in size and number of liver cells in response to normal growth—membrane synthesis. In healthy animals the synthesis of cells is stable, occurring at a predictable rate, but sudden or highly accelerated losses of certain liver cells (hepatocytes) due say to food additives—should they be deleterious—would result in metabolic difficulties altering the rate and pattern of membrane synthesis and which could be measured with great precision long before the effect became grossly discernible—if it ever did. This exquisite morphometric procedure is no more than five years down the safety testing road and, interestingly enough, the procedures are being developed in both academic and industrial laboratories.

· **Vitamins** ·

Finally, because of the widespread belief that vitamins at any level must be beneficial because they're vitamins, a word of caution. Vitamins no matter what else they may be are still chemicals and as such react with other chemicals in the body. Therefore, dose is extremely important. An excess of Vitamin D can result in serious toxicity. Vitamin D promotes absorption of calcium from the intestine, and a large excess of stored Vitamin D can cause excessive blood levels of calcium (hypercalcemia) that often persist for months after intake of the vitamin has been discontinued.

Chronic hypercalcemia can cause such diverse effects as calcification of soft tissue with particularly serious injury to the kidney, loss of appetite and constipation. Normal children, normal adults and pregnant and lactating women do not require more than 400 International Units of Vitamin D per day. This level can be easily met by exposure to sunshine and consumption of such foods as egg yolk, fish and Vitamin D fortified milk.

Among all the vitamins, probably none has generated more heat than light than Vitamin E. The list of ailments claimed to be relieved by this chemical includes such a disparate variety as heart disease, infertility, cancer, ulcers, general weakness, skin disorders and shortness of breath. And for those healthy individuals who consume Vitamin E in large quantities, there is the anticipated promise of enhanced sexual potency, freedom from heart attacks, protection from the varied effects of air pollution and slowing of the aging process with all its attendant benefits.

Would that these were so. Unfortunately, no amount of fortification with Vitamin E will achieve these hoped for benefits. Careful studies over many years attempting to relate these symptoms to a deficiency of Vitamin E in people have been unproductive. The wide distribution of this vitamin in vegetable oils, cereal grains, and animal fats makes a deficiency very unlikely.

The recommended daily allowance—RDA—for Vitamin E is five International Units for infants, twenty to twenty-five for adult women and thirty for adult men and pregnant or lactating women. An International Unit is roughly equivalent to a milligram.

Realizing how little human nature has changed over the millennium, I reached back some three hundred years for a thought that could aptly describe some of the problems of our own time. I found one in Thomas Hobbes. "There is no such thing" he wrote, "as perpetual tranquillity of mind while we live here." He was certainly correct with regard to food additives.

With the passage of the four years since this book originally appeared, I am even more convinced that our food supply is among the best, if not the best, in the world; but tranquil about it we'll never be. Perhaps that's all to the good.

As my confidence is rooted in knowledge of the lengths gone to make our food supply safe, I say, "eat hearty."

Melvin A. Benarde, Ph.D.
Princeton, New Jersey
June, 1975

PERTINENT READINGS

The Testing of Chemicals for Carcinogenicity, Mutagenicity, and Teratogenicity. Ministry of Health and Welfare, Ottawa, Ontario, 1975.

The Use of Chemicals in Food Production: Processing, Storage, and Distribution. National Academy of Sciences, Washington, D.C., 1973.

Hair Dyes Linked to Cancer. *Medical World News,* May 5, 1975, page 31.

Hazards of Overuse of Vitamin D, Committee on Nutritional Misinformation. National Academy of Sciences, Washington, D.C., 1975.

Principles for Evaluating Chemicals in the Environment: A Report of the Committee for the Working Conference on Principles of Protocols for Evaluating Chemicals in the Environment. National Academy of Sciences, Washington, D.C., 1975.

Carcinogenesis Testing of Chemicals, edited by Leon Golberg. CRC Press, Cleveland, Ohio, 1974.

Quantitative Microscopic Evaluation of the Endoplasmic Reticulum in Developing Human Liver. F. A. de la Iglesia, J. M. Sturgess, E. J. McGuire and G. Feuer, personal communication.

The
Chemicals
We Eat

CHAPTER I

Why Chemicals in Foods?

"A people never fairly begins to prosper till
necessity is treading on its heels."

SIMMS

Cranberries on Thanksgiving are as American as apple pie
and chicken chow mein. Thanksgiving without cranberries
was unthinkable until November 9, 1959, when Arthur
S. Flemming, Secretary of the Department of Health, Education, and Welfare, announced to the hastily gathered press
that Aminotriazole,* a weedicide, had been found in cranberries. Feeding rats 10 to 100 times the amount of Aminotriazole detected on the cranberries for 70 to 100 weeks
produced cancer of the thyroid in some of the animals.

---

*Aminotriazole, a weedicide long used in cornfields, prevents the formation
of chlorophyll (the green pigment plants need for photosynthesis) and
thus of carbohydrate. Without carbohydrate the weed dies.

By Thursday, the 26th, the storm of charges and counter-charges, confusion and uncertainty had become such that cranberries became untouchable to millions of Americans.

On October 18, 1969, almost exactly a decade later, Robert H. Finch, then Secretary of Health, Education, and Welfare, told the press that cyclamates, nonnutritive sweeteners we had come to accept as staples in our diets, would be banned from use in food and drink by the following January.

Because of the added anxiety engendered in a public already sensitized by fears of the effects of DDT, smoking, air and water pollution, markets couldn't give away foods containing cyclamates. Once again, studies on rats had pointed to the potential hazard. This time it was a rare form of bladder cancer that developed in seven of twenty rats fed for a lifetime on 50 times the maximum human intake of cyclamates.

Now no food is sacred, not even apple pie or chicken chow mein. A case in point is monosodium glutamate (MSG), an ingredient added to enhance the flavor of chow mein and other such dishes as egg drop soup, chicken ding ho,* and hundreds of common foods. It is currently suspected of causing "Chinese Restaurant Syndrome." †

If public paranoia continues, it is only a matter of time before apple pie itself comes under the toxicologist's scrutiny.

---

*I mention chicken ding ho because recently in Boston, while eating it for the first time, I developed severe chest pains and was taken to the Massachusetts General Hospital to be certain I did not have a myocardial infarction or other coronary complication. The diagnosis was a probable case of Chinese Restaurant Syndrome.

†"Chinese Restaurant Syndrome" is a recently discovered complex of symptoms that in various individuals produces tingling of the lips, loss of breath, fainting, and chest pains resembling heart disease.

I do not mean to sound frivolous or to imply that I consider chemicals in foods a trivial problem. I do not. On the other hand, I am not worried by their presence—and neither should you be, and I shall attempt to explain why.

The fact is that all living things are made up of chemicals —we ourselves just as much as the crops and animals we eat. Moreover, it must be remembered that nature has endowed many plants, insects, fish, shellfish, and animals with a variety of chemicals that can be harmful to man, as we shall see in Chapter 2. Some, like the fly agaric (*Amanita muscaria*), a mushroom, contain a chemical that is toxic in the smallest doses; on the other hand cauliflower, for example, contains thiocyanate, a goitrogen, whose effects do not become evident unless many pounds are consumed.

Finally, I am not worried because I know that everything is being done that can be done to ensure the safety of the chemicals used in foods.

In March, 1960, George P. Larrick, Commissioner of the Food and Drug Administration, stated quite rightly: "The general public, confused by the cranberry, caponette and black jelly bean episodes, and by misleading information from various sources, is understandably uncertain over just what the so-called chemicals in foods problem is all about." Far from having abated, the confusion, anxiety, and tension in the mind of the public has sharply increased today.

Two obvious questions suggest themselves. (1) Is it necessary to add chemicals to our foods? (2) Is our food supply safe? Unfortunately unqualified "yes" or "no" answers would be naive and misleading.

We must start by asking: "What does the consumer want?"

Today's homemaker not only casually accepts, but insists on being able to buy "instant," "heat and serve," and "ready to cook" convenience foods that her grandmother never dreamed of. One of the reasons is that more women are taking jobs—74 million of them today, and a projected 135 million in 2000 A.D. As a result they have less time to spend in the kitchen and more money to pay for the relatively more expensive convenience foods. (Disposable income in the United States has more than doubled since 1950, and it is expected to continue to rise.)

The growing stock of imported foods in supermarkets and specialty stores is evidence of a new sophistication on the part of consumers who have traveled abroad as never before. They return with a desire to introduce their friends to the dishes they have tasted and yet they are unwilling to spend the time to make them from scratch. Thus, packaged mousse and soufflé dishes, béarnaise and hollandaise sauces, quiche Lorraine, steak and kidney pie, etc., must be designed for greater shelf life. Without the addition of chemicals these exotic foods, as well as more prosaic items like frozen cakes and "instant" breakfasts, would simply not exist.

More and more foods and beverages are being sold from vending machines, and they must be stable prepared products with a long shelf life. And as a result of these snacks eaten on impulse, obesity has become a national problem in the United States. Awareness of obesity has, in turn, stimulated the demand for nonnutritive foods and sophisticated prepared foods that are low in caloric value but may include many chemical additives.

Another social trend that is encouraging the development of new types of foods is the great increase in human longevity. By 1980 it is estimated that at least 14 percent of the population in the United States—close to 35 million people—will be over sixty. This will constitute a major market for geriatric foods at prices that old people, living on savings or a fixed pension, can afford.

Perhaps the greatest stimulus to advances in food technology is our rapidly expanding population. At the turn of this century, the 45 states in the Union had a total population of 76 million. By 1960, the figure had more than doubled, and by 1980 it is expected to have doubled again. Figures 1, 2, and 3 trace the trends of U.S. population growth since 1750, world growth for the same period, and world growth since 1 A.D., respectively. Additionally, the graph for the U.S. shows the wide range of population predictions. The actual figure attained will depend upon a number of factors not easily assessed at the present time. All the figures have a common characteristic: a precipitous rise occurring around 1850. This, for the journalist, is the "population explosion."

This rapid increase carries with it a particularly ominous threat. According to the Food and Agriculture Organization of the United Nations, there is not enough food in many areas of the world for the present population. Although we in the United States are not immediately threatened, we must constantly seek new ways of wresting from the soil greater and greater yields per acre, and of defeating the microbes, insects, nematodes, and mammals that constantly vie with us for the available food supply. Consider this problem carefully when you hear the cry "banish chemicals."

In 1920, the arable land then under cultivation fed 106 million people. In 1970, an additional 105 million people are being fed from less arable land, and by the year 2000 there will be more than two mouths to feed where there was only one in 1970. Clearly, not only must more and more food be produced on less and less available land, but, perhaps even more important, what is produced must be protected

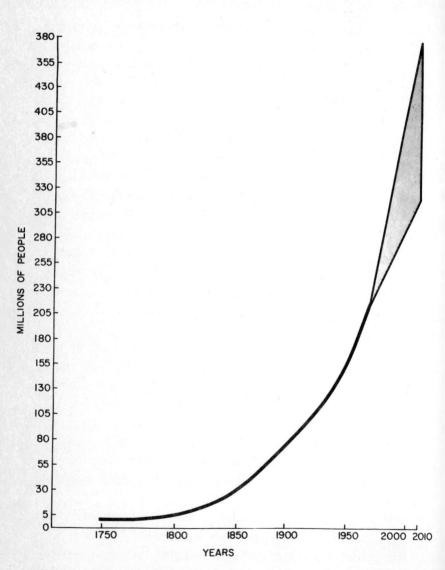

Figure 1. U.S. population growth since 1750

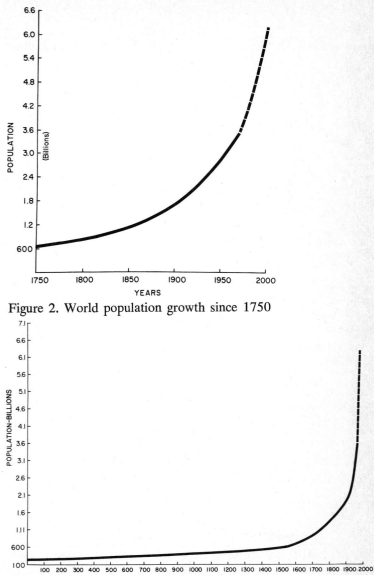

Figure 2. World population growth since 1750

Figure 3. World population growth since A.D. 1

until it can be harvested, processed, marketed, bought, and eaten.

Losses in per acre yields as a result of weeds and other pests are enormous, as Table 1 shows. Researchers at the

TABLE 1
ESTIMATED LOSSES IN SOME PRINCIPAL CROPS
(POTENTIAL PRODUCTION) U.S., 1965

| Crop | Source of Loss (percent) | | | | Loss in Tons |
	Disease	Insects	Nematodes	Weeds	(Millions)
Corn	12	12	3	10	37
Wheat	14	6		12	11.5
Rice	7	4		17	0.6
Soy bean	14	3	2	17	3.7
Dry bean	17	20		15	0.5
Snap bean	20	12	5	9	0.3
Potatoes	19	14	4	3	4.7
Tomatoes	22	7	8	7	5.0
Apples	8	13		3	0.7
Oranges	12	6	4	5	1.5
Strawberries	26	25		25	0.2
Alfalfa	24	15	3		30
Pasture & range .	5	20		15	100
(as hay equivalent)					
Sugar beets	16	12	4	8	5.9

Agricultural Experiment Station of the University of Massachusetts grew corn in plots with and without weeds. Plants in the weedless plots yielded up to 65 percent more corn than plants that had to compete with weeds for space, moisture, and nutrients. Similar tests at the University of Iowa obtained a third more corn from weed-free plots. Apply these percentages to millions of tons of crops and you will begin to appreciate the magnitude of the weed problem.

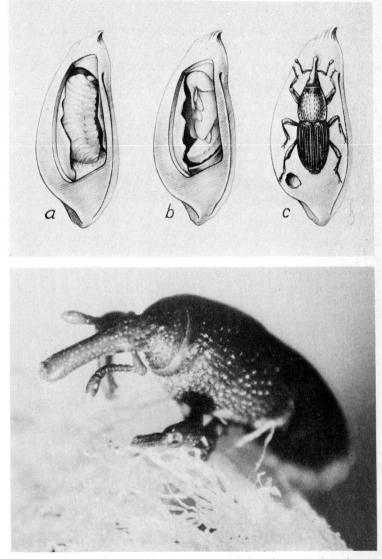

Figure 4. Life stages of the granary weevil in wheat, and a picture of *Sitophilus*, a grain weevil, much enlarged

Even with the controls now in use, insects (see Figure 4) account for losses amounting to over $500 million annually in food being stored and shipped. Destruction of food by rats costs well over $2 billion a year. Then add the value of the millions of tons of crops lost to weeds and you will see why food processors, farmers, and consumers all have a vital stake in the use of chemicals to increase our food supply.

Agricultural economists estimate that 20 to 25 percent of our annual food crop is lost to predation: either ruined on the vine or spoiled after harvest. To prevent additional losses the farmer uses the only effective means thus far available to him—chemical pesticides. In order to curtail or prevent losses in livestock, milk, and meat production by the ravages of microbes, ticks, lice, flies, and worms chemical control is vital.

Besides protecting our food supply at its source, chemicals play an important role in allowing us to stockpile produce for emergencies. Food technologists are in fact modern Josephs, evening out the fat and the lean years.

The judicious use of chemicals also affords us the luxury of finding formerly seasonal foods in markets all year round, and of prolonging the freshness of perishable produce.

It was recently pointed out that when Abraham Lincoln clerked in a country store, some 900 items could be offered to the customers. By 1941, the figure had increased to 1500, making it quite clear that people wanted variety in their diets. In 1960 we could shop for more than 6000 food items, and in 1970 the larger supermarkets offered more than 7500. Moreover, the 210 million of us are eating better now than the 106 million did in 1920. But the major factors in our ability to feed this vastly increased population better have been increased yield per acre of land and per head of live-

stock, along with the longer shelf life of food products. All
this has been accomplished with chemicals.

In my book *Our Precarious Habitat* I told of a nutritional study made in England during World War II, and the
story bears repeating here. When Britain was besieged early
in the war, the problem of feeding a nation that relied so
heavily on imports became a matter of acute anxiety. A study
was undertaken to determine the nutritional requirements of
an adequate diet. Tests on both men and women soon showed
that a simple but tedious diet of green vegetables, bread, and
milk could easily support vigorous activity. Although such
a diet would have drastically reduced the need for imported
food, it was not adopted because it was considered far too
monotonous for the maintenance of a highly advanced country
for any sustained period. A British scientist, Magnus Pike,
commented: "A diet may be perfectly balanced nutritionally,
but if it is not sufficiently attractive a workman may not eat
enough of it to do his work. If a chemist can enhance the
attractiveness of such a diet harmlessly, he is, in fact, contributing to nutritional well-being."

Today, homemakers want not only variety and convenience,
they want quality, form and palatability, color, flavor, and
texture. These high standards can only be maintained by
chemicals.

To return to the questions we posed earlier: "Is it necessary
to add chemicals to our foods?" and "Is our food supply safe?"
The answer to the first is a qualified "yes." Chemical additives
are necessary if the demands of modern homemakers are to
be met. The second question is the subject of the chapters that
follow.

CHAPTER II

A Chemical Is
a Chemical
Is a Chemical

"Quod ali cibus est aliis fiat acre veneum."
(What is food to one man may be a fierce
poison to another.)

LUCRETIUS, 95–55 B.C.

"If it's natural it must be good" is a belief accepted by more and more people who have been frightened by the reported effects of chemical sprays and additives on foods. But is this always true?

First of all "natural" is a relative word in light of the fact that all living things are composed of chemicals. Moreover, a given chemical that has been synthesized in a laboratory is indistinguishable from the same chemical that has been extracted from a plant or an animal. Thus, for example, capsules of vitamin A made by a pharmaceutical company will have the same physiologic effect as equal quantities of vitamin A absorbed by eating beef liver, chili con carne, carrots, Boston brown bread, or apricots.

Chemists have analyzed a wide range of natural foods, breaking them down into their chemical components. Cow's milk, for example, consists of lactose, phosphatase, lactalbumin, folic and nicotinic acids, and at least 95 other chemicals; what makes the housewife stream tears while peeling onions is a combination of propionaldehyde, methyl alcohol, propyl mercaptan, hydrogen sulfide, acetaldehyde, sulfur

TABLE 2
CHEMICALS CONTRIBUTING TO AROMA OF COFFEE

Acetaldehyde	Hydrogen sulfide
Acetic acid	Hydroquinone
Acetone	Isovaleric acids
Acetyl methyl carbinol	*m*-Valeric acid
Acetyl propionyl	Methyl alcohol
Ammonia	Methyl amine
Cresols	Methyl ethyl acetaldehyde
Diacetyl	Methyl ethyl acetic acid
Diethyl ketone	Methyl mercaptan
Dimethyl sulfide	*n*-Heptacosane
2,3-Dioxyacetophenone	*N*-methyl pyrrole
Esters	*p*-Vinyl guaiacol
Ethyl alcohol	Phenol
Eugenol	Pyrazine
Formic acid	Pyridine and homologues
Furane	Pyrrole
Furfural	Resorcinol
Furfuryl acetate	Resorcinol
Furfuryl alcohol	Sylvestrine
Furfuryl mercaptan	Trimethylamine
Guaiacol	Vanillone
Higher fatty acids	

dioxide, dipropyl disulfide, and propyl alcohol; the aroma of freshly brewed coffee has been broken down into some forty chemical components (see Table 2), and researchers are still not through. The bite in horseradish is caused by the chemical allyl isothiocyanate. Raw beef takes its color from the large protein molecule myoglobin which is closely related to the hemoglobin that pigments red blood cells. The yellow, orange, and orange-red fat-soluble pigments known as the carotenoids give their distinctive color to carrots, tomatoes, squash, banana skins, red peppers, peaches, and sweet potatoes, as well as orange, yellow, and red flowers. The anthocyanin pigments color beets, red cabbage, black mulberry, and vinifera grapes; the green of green beans, peas, spinach, etc., is supplied by chlorophylls, whereas the anthoxanthins are the pigments in onion skins, tea, yellow corn, oranges, lemons, parsley, and yellow dahlias. The examples could be multiplied endlessly.

That chemicals in foods are "natural" does not preclude the fact that they can be hazardous and even toxic to man, as even the ancients recognized. When, for example, the "elders" decided that Socrates was too disturbing an influence on the Athenian community, he was handed an extract of *Conium maculatum*—the hemlock plant—with which to dispatch himself to a more propitious environment. Although hemlock's toxic properties were well established by 399 B.C., it was not until more modern times that Coniine (2-propyl-piperidine) was isolated and found to be the "active (dis-patching) principle." Why nature in her infinite wisdom endowed trees, plants, insects, animals, and fish—many of which are part of our food supply—with chemicals potentially toxic to man remains a mystery. What physiologic and/or biochemical function these "toxic" chemicals play in the total

Figure 5. Oranges and grapefruits summarized chemically

economy of plants and animals still remains one of nature's
closely guarded secrets.

The point of these examples is that although we call a
number of plants and animals "food," they are in fact chemicals, as are all living things. What remains to be discovered
is how they are put together to assume their unique form.
But whether synthesized by a cow or a chemist lactose is still
$C_{12}H_{22}O_{11}$, and sorbic acid is $C_6H_8O_2$ whether obtained from
a mountain ash or a laboratory. Differentiation cannot be made
by any chemical procedure. As the title of this chapter notes,
a chemical is a chemical is a chemical.

To carry this one step further, most people take vitamins
for granted and many even buy them to supplement their
diets, believing they are not getting enough from the foods
they eat. However, the vitamins too are chemicals, with some
of the most difficult names and complex formulas. Table 3
lists the major vitamins with their common and technical
designations. It is obvious they are very chemical. In fact
because there is such a demand for vitamins seven of the
eight are fabricated commercially. And is there anyone who
believes that vitamins can be harmful? Perhaps the following
account may be instructive.

As the crew walked down the gangplank, after weeks at
sea, few of those waiting at the pier to greet them would have
believed that vitamin A was responsible for the dreadful
condition of the men's skin.

According to Dr. J. P. Nater of The Hague, Netherlands,
a Dutch trawler fishing in the North Atlantic off the Norwegian
coast had landed a halibut some 6 feet wide. The fish provided the main course at dinner for eleven of the twelve men
aboard.

One of the men ate two-thirds of a pound of the liver, con-

TABLE 3

VITAMIN NONMENCLATURE

Common Name	Chemical Designation	Formula	Natural Source
Vitamin A	*Retinol* 3,7-dimethyl-9-(2,6,6,-trimethyl-1-cyclohexen-1-yl)-2,4,6,8-nonatetraen-1-ol	$C_{20}H_{30}O$	Fish, liver, eggs, Provitamin A(carotene) found in many plants
Vitamins B			
B_1	*Thiamine hydrochloride* 3-(4-Amino-2-methylpyrimidyl-5-methyl)-4-methyl-5-(-hydroxyethyl) thiazolium chloride hydrochloride	$C_{12}H_{17}ClN_4OS \cdot HCl$	Pork, ham, peas, eggs, cereals
B_2	*Riboflavin* 7,8-Dimethyl-10-(D-ribo-2,3,4,5-tetrahydroxypentyl) isoalloxazine	$C_{17}H_{20}N_4O_6$	Milk, eggs, malted barley, yeast
B_5	*Pantothenic acid* N-(2,4-Dihydroxy-3,3-dimethyl butyryl) alanine	$C_9H_{17}NO_5$	Jelly of queen bee, liver, rice bran, molasses
B_6	*Pyridoxine hydrochloride* 5-Hydroxy-6-methyl-3,4-pyride dimethanol hydro-chloride	$C_8H_{11}NO \cdot HCl$	Yeast, liver, cereals
B_{12}	*Cyanocobalamin* 5,6-dimethylbenzi-midazolyl cyanocobamide	$C_{63}H_{38}CoN_{14}O_{14}P$	Liver, kidney
Vitamin C	*Ascorbic Acid*	$C_6H_8O_6$	Citrus Fruit
Vitamin D	*Calciferol*	$C_{28}H_{44}O$	Fish oils
Vitamin E	*Alpha-tocopherol* 2,5,7,8 Tetramethyl-2-(4',2',12'-trimethyl tridecyl)-6-chromanol	$C_{24}H_{50}O_2$	Lettuce, alfalfa, seed germ oils

taining approximately 30 million units of vitamin A—the equivalent of 2,000 vitamin tablets. Shortly after eating, the symptoms of hypervitaminosis A hit all eleven men: nausea, vomiting, and headaches were followed by red, swollen skin. The following morning large sheets of skin began peeling off. When the trawler reached port ten days later, the men's skin was still sloughing. Imagine, vitamin A, a natural toxicant!

In Dr. Leon Goldberg's Milroy Lecture, "The Amelioration of Food," given before the Royal College of Physicians,* he listed the content of carcinogenic 3,4-benzpyrene contained in a number of natural foods as follows:

	Micrograms† per Kilogram (mg/kg)
cabbage	13–25
lettuce	3–13
spinach	8
leek	7
tea	4

Unfortunately calculations suggesting that natural foods are safe because one would have to eat 20 to 30 pounds in order to obtain a toxic dose fail to take into account possible combined effects of groups of compounds occurring together.

This sets the issue squarely; the amount consumed is central to the issue of what constitutes a toxicant or a poison.

The concept was first framed by Lucretius in *De Rerum Natura (On the Nature of Things)*. He wrote: "Quod ali cibus est aliis fiat acre veneum"—what is food to one man may

---

*London, 1967.
† 1000 micrograms = 1 milligram
  1000 milligrams = 1 gram
    30 grams = 1 ounce
      1 milligram per kilogram (2.2 pounds) = 1 part per million (ppm)
      1 drop in 80 fifths of whiskey = 1 part per million

be a fierce poison to another. This remains the issue today, whether we are talking of natural foods or food additives.

Much of the research into the chemistry of natural foods has turned up substances which are frightening only because they are so hard to spell and pronounce. But as noted, a number of natural foods have been found to contain potentially toxic chemicals that can cause a range of responses from slight discomfort to death. The toxins include lathrogens, gossypol, enzyme inhibitors, cyanogens, hemaglutinins, vasoconstrictors, allergens, and even estrogenic compounds. In some instances, the chemical is present at such low levels that a daily intake of some 20 to 30 pounds of the food would be required to produce a reaction in a susceptible individual. In others, a few mouthfuls will do the damage.

Some chemicals, such as the cyanide found in lima beans, can be deactivated by the heat of cooking. In other instances it has been found that the toxic chemical appears only at a certain stage of development. Unripe grapefruit, for example, contains a potentially hazardous chemical not found in the mature fruit. In still other instances the toxin-containing portions of the plant or animal tissue can be removed. Thus, by peeling potatoes that have been exposed to sunlight, the toxin solanine, found in the skin and sprouts, can be avoided.

The skins of number of fish contain a powerful ichthyosarcotoxin. Consequently, restaurant cooks must have a license to prepare these fish so that clients will run no risk of tetradon poisoning. Similarly, oysters, clams, and mussels are known to contain toxic paralytic substances when grown under certain conditions, and extracts of certain oysters have proved lethal to mice on intraperitoneal injection.

Accordingly, it is curious that, in spite of this knowledge and its long history, a number of people continue to advocate in stentorian tones that whatever is natural is safe. Even more curious is the fact that a segment of the public accepts this without question.

In the ensuing discussion of the major categories of toxins found in natural foods, the injunction "if it's natural it must be safe" will be examined.

· Cyanogens ·

Strange as it may appear, hydrogen cyanide (HCN) is a constituent of a large number of edible plants. Cyanogens or the cyanogenetic glucosides, which on hydrolysis (splitting) in the human intestine yield cyanide, are found in such garden-variety foodstuffs as lima beans, sweet potatoes, yams, sugar cane, peas, cherries, plums, and apricots. What function these cyanide-containing compounds play in the growth and metabolism of the plants is one of the intriguing questions chemists have for years been trying to answer.

Although most university-level biochemistry courses cover the glucosides and frequently discuss amygdalin as an example of this class of compounds, few, if any, students probably remember that on hydrolysis (splitting of the glucoside into its components) it releases HCN. And further, few associate the release of cyanide with its potential for human toxicity. Interestingly enough, whereas maximum yields of amygdalin are obtained from almonds, it is also found in significant amounts in the kernels of such fruits as the cherry, plum, apricot, apple, pear, lemon, and lime.

The initial symptoms of acute cyanogen poisoning have been described as numbness in fingertips and toes and giddiness or lightheadedness. If the dose is large enough, this is followed by mental confusion, stupor, cyanosis, twitching convulsions (indication that the central nervous system is involved), and in the terminal phase coma and death. This clinical complex is related to an oral minimum lethal dose of HCN ranging from 0.5 to 3.5 mg/kg (0.5 to 3.5 ppm). The lethal dose is estimated to be upwards of 7 ppm (mg/kg).

Small, nonfatal doses often produce headache, sensations of tightness in both throat and chest, perceptible heart beating (palpitations), and general weakness. Full recovery is usual as the body processes eliminate the offending chemical.

For a number of years sporadic reports have hinted at the possibility of chronic cyanogen intoxication. Most recently studies in a cassava-eating area of Nigeria have implicated cyanogen poisoning most directly with ataxia—a loss of muscular coordination.

Medical case reports have from time to time suggested the association of amblyopia (partial loss of sight and diminution of vision) with chronic cassava intoxication. Evidence now appears to point to a relationship between a state of general nutritional deprivation and the consumption of only trace amounts of a cyanogen as necessary to elicit clinical symptoms.

The acute toxic properties of cassava, for example, have been known for hundreds of years, and there are also abundant records of acute poisoning from the ingestion of peach kernels and bitter almonds. This, in conjunction with reports of experimental animal trials, leaves little doubt that the release of HCN is the prime cause of intoxication.

However, cassava is not in the same category as the fruits noted above. Even when eaten in gluttonous quantities, those fruits would be most unlikely to elicit any of the symptoms mentioned even in the most sensitive of individuals.

More recently, the possible combined effects of HCN from cigarette smoke, polluted air, and food consumption has been quantitatively considered in terms of man's total exposure.

Fortunately evidence suggests that the body can adequately cope with the burden.

· **Goitrogens** ·

While it is well known that a lack of iodine in the diet can lead to the goitrous condition hypothyrodism, it is not widely appreciated that eating cabbage, cauliflower, turnips, mustard and collard greens, and brussel sprouts may induce goiter formation in susceptible individuals.

These plants and others of the *Cruciferae* family, including kale, broccoli, rutabaga, kohlrabi, radish, and horseradish, contain thioglucosides which, under certain conditions, can block the absorption of iodine. A number of scientific reports suggest the association of goiter with the consumption of cruciferous plants, but a cause and effect relationship has yet to be proved. The chemical thiocyanate is particularly abundant in cauliflower, but it would require a daily intake of between 22 and 25 pounds of the vegetable before the blood thiocyanate level would rise to the danger point. Experiments have shown that feeding large quantities of crucifers to test animals can induce hypothyroidism, but the problem of extrapolating those results to human illness is a thorny one as we shall see, in another context, in Chapter 4.

· **Pressor Amines** ·

Chemical analysis of such seemingly innocuous foods as bananas and various cheeses reveals the presence of a number of esoteric organic chemicals including the amines * histamine and tyramine. These are called pressor amines because of their ability to constrict the blood vessels quickly and elevate the blood pressure dramatically. It is not unusual to isolate 100 to 200 milligrams† of tyramine from 100 grams (a little less than 0.25 pound) of camembert cheese. If this amount of tyramine were injected directly into the bloodstream we could expect an immediate rise in blood pressure. But this does not happen to the person who eats 0.25 pound of camembert at a single sitting. Their ingestion and passage into the stomach and absorption therefrom mitigates what otherwise could result in a stunning physiologic response.

In the past few years we have learned at least one of the ways in which these pressor amines are detoxified in the body. It appears that monoamine oxidase (MAO), an enzyme, oxidizes them into para-hydroxyphenylacetic acid, which is not a vasoconstrictor. However, there are cases on record of serious and sometimes fatal illness on the part of people taking tranquilizing drugs who had also eaten aged cheese, beer, or wine, high in tyramine content. It is now known that certain

---

*The amines are derivatives of ammonia in which the hydrogen atoms have been replaced by alkyl or aryl groups and the nitrogen is directly attached to the carbon.

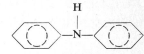

H	H	
H—N—H	H_3C—N—H	diphenylamine
ammonia	methylamine	

They are widely distributed in nature, and the decomposition of many natural products, such as proteins, leads to their formation. Decaying fish has the distinct odor of trimethylamine.

Amino acids contain both an amino (—NH_2) and a carboxyl (—COOH) group and are the building blocks from which proteins are formed.

† 1000 micrograms = 1 milligram
  454 grams = 1 pound.

tranquilizers can chemically inhibit or block the enzyme MAO, thus permitting the nonoxidized pressor amines access to the bloodstream. As a consequence, people on tranquilizers are now generally advised to restrict their intake of a number of cheeses and fermented beverages.

· Gossypol ·

The genus *Gossypium* contains all the cotton plants cultivated around the world. Cotton plants yield, in addition to fiber, enormous tonnages of both oil and high-protein meal for human and animal consumption. Because of the increasing concern for additional sources of protein to alleviate worldwide protein shortages, attention is being directed to the large supplies of cottonseed meal with its high concentration of available protein.

Cottonseed is the most widely distributed oilseed in many underdeveloped areas of the world, and so it lends itself to the production of flour and such other products as Incaparina,* a high-protein, low-cost beverage that can be made locally to upgrade nutritional standards.

However, reports of injury to livestock that have consumed cottonseed meal go back more than a century. More recently

---

*Incaparina is made of cottonseed flour and whole ground cooked corn. It is about 25 percent protein, and 100 grams supply 370 calories. It was developed in Guatemala from locally available materials by the Instituto de Nutrición de Centro America y Panama (INCAP). Laubina, whose basic ingredients are wheat and chick peas, is another high-protein beverage of the same kind. It was produced by Columbia University's Institute of Nutrition Research at the American University in Beirut, Lebanon.

it has been discovered that the yellow pigment, gossypol,*
is the active principle of the meal. In subsequent studies the
pigment has been shown to be highly toxic to animals,
and it has been incriminated to account for the olive green
discoloration of egg yolks produced by hens fed on cottonseed meal containing 0.4 to 0.5 percent by weight of gossypol.
As a consequence, cottonseed products intended for human
consumption now may not exceed 0.045 percent of gossypol
by weight.

· **Lathyrogens** ·

Lathyrism, a spastic paralysis of the legs, comes from
Lathyrus, the Latin name for certain members of the pea
family long recognized as having toxic qualities. Hippocrates
noted the deleterious effects of some peas, and Hindu writings
allude to the crippling lameness that resulted from eating
such legumes as peas, beans, and lentils. *Lathyrus sativa*, the
chick pea, *Lathyrus cicera*, the flat-podded vetch, and *L.
clymenum*, the Spanish vetchling, are three of the more widely

---

*Chemically gossypol is 1,1′,6,6′,7,7′-hexahydroxy-5,5′-diisopropyl-3,3′-di-
methyl-(2,2′-binaphthalene)-8,8′-dicarboxaldehyde. Graphically, the structure
of the formula $C_{30}H_{30}O_8$, is

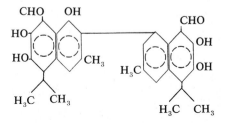

eaten species of *Lathyrus* from which lathrogens can be isolated.

In India, for example, lathyrism has the status of a public health problem, particularly during famines when chick pea meal is widely relied upon to sustain large numbers of destitute people for extended periods. Being an unusually hardy plant, the chick pea survives the long dry spells that eliminate other food crops. Regular and continued consumption of chick pea meal results in muscular weakness and spastic paralysis of the legs, with death ensuing in extreme cases.

Current medical opinion suggests that the lathrogen, beta-N-oxalyl-L-alpha$_1$-beta-diaminopropionic acid, a neurotoxic amino acid, is the substance in the chick peas and vetch responsible for lathyrism.

Because of dietary preferences and an abundant food supply, lathyrism is not seen in the Unted States or Western Europe; and it is not anticipated that it will be in the future.

• Hemaglutenins •

For hundreds of years an acute form of hemolytic anemia (a breaking down of the red blood cells) has existed among peoples living in countries bordering the Mediterranean. The particular form that is triggered by ingestion of the fava bean (*Vicia faba*) appears to be unique to the area, and is notably evident in Sardinia, which reports the highest number of new cases yearly. This is particularly curious because the fava bean is grown and eaten almost the world over.

The hemolytic attack generally begins some 8 hours after the beans are eaten (6 to 25 hours is the reported range). Indeed, only a small amount of fava protein can trigger an attack. Dizziness, chills, pallor, and vomiting are the early symptoms; in the most severe cases jaundice and hemoglobinuria * are evident. Adults generally recover completely after two uncomfortable days, but the disease is fatal to between six and eight of any 100 children affected.

The curious geographic selectivity of the fava bean's pernicious effect has now been shown to be genetically determined. It appears that an inherited metabolic defect has left certain people with a deficiency of glucose-6-phosphate dehydrogenase (G6PD), an enzyme usually found in red blood cells which aids in maintaining their structural integrity. People with little or no G6PD are particularly susceptible to hemolytic diseases engendered by a variety of chemicals. Evidently the fava bean contains one of these chemicals, although that chemical has not yet been identified.

· **Mushrooms** ·

Mushroom lovers (mycophiles) are well aware of the danger inherent in sampling wild mushrooms. Botanists have described more than twenty-five highly toxic species of amanita, including *Amanita phalloides*, the Death Angel.

The content of phalloidine in the Death Angel produces rapid degeneration of kidney, liver, and heart muscles; and the symptoms—before death mercifully ensues—are most grotesque.

---

*Hemoglobinuria is a red to black discoloration of the urine that results from the breaking down of the red blood corpuscles and the consequent release of hemoglobin.

• Animal Tissue Toxins •

Toxic substances exist in animal tissues. Both finned fish and shellfish provide a veritable treasury of naturally toxic substances that can trigger anything from a simple allergic reaction to paralysis and death.

Tetradon poisoning, contracted by eating any of the puffer fishes, is characterized by the sudden onset of tingling and numbness in lips and tongue followed by a loss of coordination and by nausea, vomiting, convulsions, paralysis, and often death. The puffers, including balloon fishes, fugu, and toadfish, contain substances in their skins (ichthyosarcotoxins) that can be poisonous to man.

Because fugu is considered a delicacy by the Japanese, and because a large number of people succumb to its toxin each year, Japanese restaurants serving it must employ a chef certified to prepare it.

Ciguatera and scombroid poisoning result from the ingestion of fish that have themselves eaten or developed toxic chemicals.

Such fish as the snapper, barracuda, parrotfish, surgeonfish, etc., that have eaten toxin-containing algae may transmit ciguatera poisoning to man. Since the toxin is insensitive to heat, cooking the fish does not help. One to four hours after eating, many people report numbness and tingling sensations that spread from face to lips to fingers and toes. This is followed by the usual series of responses—nausea, vomiting, and diarrhea—by which the body attempts to throw off irritating foreign chemicals.

Depending upon the concentration of toxin and the susceptibility of the individual, muscular paralysis, respiratory distress, and convulsions can occur. In some instances, death ensues. If the individual recovers, muscular weakness and tingling of face and lips can persist for several weeks. There are several recorded cases of patients who believe that cold objects are hot and hot objects are cold to the touch.

The cause of scombroid poisoning is limited to fish from tropical waters. Fresh tuna, bonita, mackerel, and skipjack, all members of the family *Scombridae*, can undergo bacterial decomposition if not promptly and adequately refrigerated. Given optimum conditions, bacteria multiply and metabolize the naturally occurring amino acid histidine to the highly toxic amine, saurine. Unfortunately this type of decomposition is not detectable in the normal way, so that the fish may be eaten without suspicion. Susciptible individuals will develop large, red, intensely itchy welts (urticaria) about the body. If death from shock does not result, victims usually recover in a day. In less acute cases, the symptoms will be the same as those noted above for ciguatera poisoning.

No discussion of naturally occurring toxins would be complete without mentioning the impressive variety of marine invertebrates, such as *Gymnodinium brevis*, the dinoflagellate protozoan responsible for the toxic "red tides" seen in waters around the world every few years. When *Gonyaulax catenella* is consumed by mussels and the mussels are eaten by humans, respiratory paralysis can occur within 10 minutes.

Then there are the sea anemones whose venom is not destroyed by heat: the sea urchin, *paracentrotus,* found off the Irish coast, and sea cucumbers with their content of holothurin.

A number of cockles, mussels, clams, and oysters can become harbingers of toxic substances as a result of their own dining; although they themselves do not react to the toxin, man does when he consumes the shellfish.

Some mammals, particularly those of the polar regions, the Eskimo dog, the sea lion, and the polar bear, have induced poisoning in man. Ironic as it may seem, the toxicant in each case was the unusually high concentration of vitamin A found in their livers. The same is also true of the livers of certain fishes, notably the halibut, as we have already seen.

· Aflatoxicosis ·

In 1960, an estimated 100,000 turkeys died in England from a sudden unexplained disease. Autopsies of the dead birds revealed major pathologic lesions of the liver, particularly acute necrosis and hemorrhage, as well as bile duct hyperplasia.*

As the cause of death could not be determined, it was called turkey "X" disease. Shortly thereafter, mass deaths of ducklings and chickens were reported, and before long a similar liver disease was reported in calves, cattle, and swine. Curiously enough, sheep proved uniquely resistant.

For the next five years turkey "X" became the subject of one of the most intensive international investigations ever launched. Before long it was demonstrated that all the animals had been fed a ration containing peanut meal contaminated with the fungus *Aspergillus flavus*. It was then found that this mold produced a highly potent toxin that was lethal

---

*Hyperplasia is a nontumorous multiplication of cells that enlarges the affected organ.

to a variety of poultry and domestic farm animals, particularly younger ones. Furthermore, those animals not killed by the toxin (including laboratory rats) developed cancer.

To denote its origin from *A. flavus*, the toxin was called aflatoxin. It was found to affect a large number of grains and beans in storage or in the field, in the presence of high moisture which favors the growth of aspergillus.

If extrapolation of animal data to man is practicable, the carcinogenic quality of aflatoxin could be significant. Accordingly, experimental animals have been fed toxin-containing rations so that researchers might assess tissues and by-products. Several studies indicate that milk from cows fed such rations contained a chemical toxic to ducklings. But in the years since turkey "X" first appeared, there has been no evidence of a similar disease in humans.

·   Ergotism   ·

St. Anthony's fire, or ergotism, is caused by *Claviceps purpurea*, a mold that grows on rye as well as on other cereal grains. The mold growing on the grain produces the chemical ergot whose active principles are a number of alkaloids built around the basic nucleus of lysergic acid. If you recall that LSD is lysergic acid diethylamide you may well imagine the symptoms experienced by some 300 inhabitants of Pont Saint Esprit, France, who contracted ergotism between August 12 and August 20, 1951. A number thought they could fly, and climbed to the rooftops to try, with fatal results. Three died and fifty became insane as a result of the hallucinations generated by the drug. Others recovered after bouts of violent nightmares.

One of the alkaloids of ergot, ergotamine, has long been used to check hemorrhaging, especially after childbirth, and because of its well known potency as a muscle contractant has also been used to induce abortion.* However, when rye or wheat flour containing claviceps is baked, the heat of the oven transforms ergotamine to $C_{15}H_{15}N_2CON(C_2H_5)_2$ which is the chemical formula for LSD. Ergotism was once one of the most common diseases in Central Europe, although now it is something of a rarity.† Still, a batch of contaminated flour could slip through if an untrained eye failed to detect the fungus growing on the grain.

· **Salmonellosis** ·

Paralleling the fungal contamination of grains and beans is bacterial contamination of food during processing. Salmonellosis and botulism are the major hazards resulting from inadequate attention to hygiene and a lack of technical proficiency. Of these, salmonellosis is much more widespread, whereas botulism is more deadly.

Probably the most important factors contributing to salmonella infections are population increase and the desire to spend less and less time in the kitchen. The processed foods that meet these needs are often distributed nationally or even internationally, so that in case of an error, oversight, or care-

---

*Ergotamine is a very powerful drug. Unless it is taken in correct doses under the guidance of a doctor, it can bring about sudden and violent death.
†Ergotism is almost entirely unknown in the United States where methods have been developed to eliminate it from grain. We are further protected by the vigilance of the Department of Agriculture and Food and Drug Administration grain inspectors, millers, and grain elevator men.

less hygiene, salmonellosis can effect large numbers of people far from the processing plant. Moreover, because conditions within the container are ideal for the survival and multiplication of the bacteria, infection and illness can occur long after the food has left the plant. It should therefore be no mystery why geographically separated outbreaks of salmonellosis are actually due to a common source.

The more than 1300 known types of salmonella can be classified into three main divisions: those strictly adapted to man; those adapted to a variety of animals; and those that infect both man and animals with equal facility. For the purpose of this discussion we can limit ourselves to the first and third.

Of the salmonella strictly adapted to man, *S. typhi* and *S. paratyphi* A & C are the prototypes. *S. typhi* is associated with typhoid fever, which is primarily a water-borne infection but can also be transmitted by contaminated food. A case in point was the epidemic in Glasgow, Scotland, in the summer of 1964, that was caused by contaminated canned corned beef imported from Argentina.

In this instance, which can serve as a model, the 5-pound cans of hot cooked beef were placed directly into water to cool. The heat of cooking had expanded the seams of the cans and the unchlorinated cooling water leaked into the beef. Unfortunately, the water was drawn from a nearby stream that was contaminated by feces containing typhoid bacteria—*Salmonella typhi*.*

In the Glasgow market, the cans were opened and portions of corned beef sold. As a consequence, the slicing machine

---

*Fecal contamination of waterways is esthetically unpleasing, but feces without microorganisms capable of causing disease are not a health hazard.

TRANSMISSION OF SALMONELLOSIS

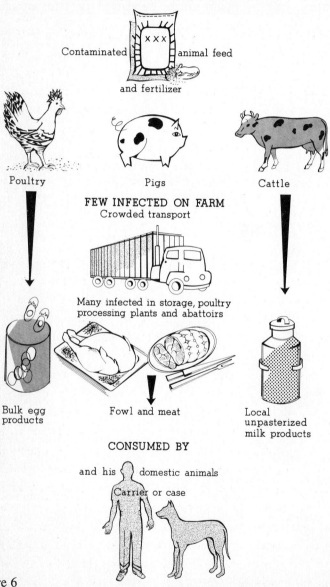

Contaminated ✗✗✗ animal feed
and fertilizer

Poultry   Pigs   Cattle

FEW INFECTED ON FARM
Crowded transport

Many infected in storage, poultry
processing plants and abattoirs

Bulk egg   Fowl and meat   Local
products   unpasteurized
                                         milk products

CONSUMED BY

and his domestic animals
Carrier or case

Figure 6

became contaminated and inoculated other meats with the bacteria.

Typhoid fever is an acute generalized infection with chills, fever (often to 104° or 105°), malaise, and headache as the initial symptoms. These are followed by crops of discrete, rounded, rose-colored spots on the chest and abdomen, which fade on pressure. It takes the disease approximately two weeks to run its course. Complications leading to death occur in 20 to 30 percent of untreated cases.

Salmonellosis, or salmonella gastroenteritis, is a more wide-spread problem for it is transmitted only by the anal-oral route. This is to say that the malevolent bacteria in the intestines of man or animals are expelled in the feces. For the infection to be passed on those feces must be ingested. Thus unhygienic food handlers in processing plants, bakeries, and restaurants are a major source of inoculation of the bacteria into food. For this reason Federal food inspectors pay particular attention to the sanitary facilities in the plants they visit and the standards of hygiene maintained by the workers there.

The largest single reservoir of salmonellae in animals prob-ably exists in domestic fowl. As a result, the sources most frequently incriminated in food-borne outbreaks of gastro-enteritis are poultry and poultry products. Figure 6 shows the now established pathways of transmission of salmonellosis.

The symptoms of salmonellosis usually appear 24 to 48 hours after ingestion of food containing, most frequently, *S. typhimurium*. The symptoms—diarrhea, abdominal cramps, and vomiting—are a response to the toxic protein elaborated by the bacteria, and are the body's way of purging itself of this foreign substance. It is at the extremes of the age groups that salmonellosis shows how nasty it can be. If the diarrhea and resulting dehydration are severe enough, particularly in older people and infants, death ensues.

The problem is that salmonella bacteria do not make their presence known through off odors and tastes, as the three epidemics described below indicate.

The symptoms noted above became unbearably familiar to some 1800 people in New York City in April, 1967, as a result of eating an imitation ice cream dessert. Its ingredients included unpasturized egg yolks which had not been cooked during the ice-cream manufacturing process.

In July, 1966, 107 people in Spokane, Washington, became ill and two died after eating barbecued chicken.

On Saturday, June 6, 1970, an outbreak of salmonella gastroenteritis involved 700 people who had attended a barbecue in Columbia, South Carolina. Although the bacteria was recovered from the feces of the victims, none of the many foods eaten at the barbecue has yet been implicated. This highlights the difficulty often encountered in trying to trace an outbreak to its source.

Public health authorities believe that the full extent of the problem is not known because salmonellosis is not a legally reportable disease. However, estimates of infection are as high as two million cases each year in the U.S. alone.

Recently a uniquely illustrative case was brought to my attention. An infant had recovered from a bout of salmonellosis after a hospital stay. Several days after the child was taken home three men from the Epidemic Surveillance Unit of the National Center for Disease Control in Atlanta, Georgia, arrived to try to discover how the child had contracted the disease.

After inspecting the kitchen and closely noting the condition of pots, pans, and dishes, they told the mother that her kitchen appeared to be in excellent condition. Could she tell them where she purchased the baby food she used? She did, and they visited the market. They made a show of shopping, but in fact they were watching the baby food shelves. Before too long they saw women, indeed mothers, come to the shelves, unscrew the caps of baby food jars, dip into them with a finger, taste the food, and then replace the caps!

The inspectors gathered a number of baby food jars and took them to the regional laboratory for testing. The dimple of the fingertip was still evident in a number of them, and on bacteriological sampling, salmonella organisms were found. The chain of transmission of the disease became clearer— appallingly so. Consider for a moment that the presence of salmonella on fingers can be the result only of contact with fecal material. This immediately implicates these women in a gross violation of the most elementary personal hygiene. Consider further that at least in the United States we are dealing with a highly literate population in which cleanliness (supposedly) has been not only our watchword but almost our religion, if television commercials are any guide.

To verify the accuracy of the incident described, it is necessary only to move slowly and unobtrusively through any supermarket. You will be astounded at the number of people who actually eat their way along the aisles.

These incidents are a sad commentary on our behavior: we demand absolute purity and safety on the one hand, and we foul our own nest on the other. Has our educational system been remiss? Somewhere along the line we seem to have lost not only our way, but perhaps more important, our sense of values.

· **Botulism** ·

Years can pass without a single reported case of botulism, but when it does occur it most often leads to the swift death of its unsuspecting victims.

Although human botulism was first recognized as related to contaminated sausage (Latin *botulus* = sausage), its rare occurrences in the U.S. can most often be traced to low-acid canned foods and more recently to smoked fish products.

Botulinus intoxication is quite different from salmonella poisoning.* The botulinus bacteria produce a toxin so potent that less than 1/100,000 of a gram can kill a mouse. There are 454 grams in 1 pound, so the toxic quantity would be barely visible to the naked eye.

The microbe *Clostridium botulinum* is naturally present in soil and lakes. It gains entrance to canned, bottled, or packaged foods as a result of insufficient cleaning or washing of the food to be processed. The bacteria prefer the low-oxygen environment of canned foods, where they produce large amounts of toxin that become intimately dispersed in the food.

Botulism almost invariably develops according to a classic pattern. Low-acid foods are inadequately heated in processing, then stored for several months before being eaten with only a cursory heating. Home-canned string beans, corn, spinach, and asparagus account for over half the reported outbreaks. Contaminated food most often lacks a telltale putrid odor,

---

*Ptomaine poisoning is a misnomer that should have passed out of use many years ago. Ptomaines, a class of foul-smelling nitrogenous chemical compounds, are not involved in food-borne illness.

and only a "sharp" or "bitter" taste is reported from time to time by victims. Usually within 12 hours of eating, the toxin begins to affect the nervous system. Vertigo, pain in the pharynx, and blurred and double vision (diplopia) are most often followed by difficulty in breathing and swallowing. Slurred speech is a frequent symptom if the dose of toxin is large, and death from respiratory collapse rapidly follows if antitoxin is not administered early enough.

While botulism is a rare illness in the continental U.S., it is almost endemic among the Eskimos of Alaska where it is caused by several of their delicacies. In these instances, the foods have had a distinct odor, but the definition of "off" or foul odors often depends on one's culture. One of the delicacies is salmon egg cheese, or "stink eggs," prepared by smoking and crushing salmon roe, and then allowing it to ferment in wooden barrels for several weeks. When it is no longer gummy, that is, when it no longer sticks to the teeth, the "cheese" is ready to eat. Another incriminated food is seal flippers, or Utjak. The flippers are allowed to remain in drums of seal oil until the skin falls loose. At this point they are ready to eat.

The rapidity of the toxic effects of these and other Eskimo foods is evident in the recent case of an Alaskan Eskimo who complained of double vision on the evening of June 3, 1970, and died in a hospital on June 6. The 54-year-old victim, his wife, and child had eaten Mikiyuk—fermented whale meat, blubber, and skin—during the afternoon of June 2. By the next day, the man was seeing double, and 24 hours later he was slurring his speech and breathing with difficulty. He was hospitalized on June 6 and died that evening before antitoxin could be administered.

Among recent cases of botulism here was that of a 25-year-old woman in Colorado Springs, Colorado. On June 20, 1970, she received a jar of home-preserved chili peppers from which she prepared a chili sandwich. Unfortunately she was undeterred by the distinct foul odor of the peppers. On the next morning, her vision was blurred, she was unable to speak and had difficulty breathing. Although she suffered a cardiac arrest, she was successfully resuscitated and maintained on a respirator and antitoxin.

From this sampling of toxins present in natural foods and the toxic substances that can develop in them during the most basic processing, it is clear that simply because a food contains no chemical additives does not necessarily mean that it is safe. On the other hand, it should also be evident that it is the quantity of the substance present, not its mere presence, that can make the natural food a hazard. And, as we shall see in Chapter 5, exactly the same thing is true of chemical additives.

CHAPTER III

What's In a Name?

"Names," says an old maxim, "are things."—
They certainly are influences. Impressions are
left and opinions are shaped by them.

TYRON EDWARDS

Of all the problems related to food, the one most hotly debated in the press is food additives. By these I mean the chemicals intentionally added to foods during manufacture to retard or prevent spoilage or to enhance flavor, texture, or nutritional quality.* Unintentional additives can be chemical spray residues not completely removed from the crop during processing or chemicals that find their way into the finished product from the wrapper or other packaging material.

---

*They are also used to thicken, soften, color, bleach, leaven, clarify, acidify, neutralize, dry, moisten, foam, prevent rancidity, and emulsify.

When I speak of intentional additives I am not referring to the adulterants that a processor might include to defraud the consumer by masking off odors and tastes.

Unfortunately, chemical additives are usually discussed with more heat than light. But despite emotional outcries against them, they are not part of a pernicious plot by food manufacturers to deceive the public. The simple fact is that processors do not have a special food supply; they eat the same food available to all of us.

Because the distance between producer and consumer can be great, because many foods are available only at certain times of the year, and because foods are chemicals and chemicals do react with each other, many problems must be overcome if the consumer is to get a container of edible food each time he picks one off a market shelf.

The trouble is that consumers reading the fine print on the labels tend to think of the ingredients as "good" or "bad" without really understanding what they are. Too often their judgment is based solely on the length of the name or the difficulty they have pronouncing it. I suspect a potential buyer seeing a label containing the ingredient cyclopentanoperhydrophenanthrene would drop the item as if it were a red-hot poker. However, if she knew that this is the chemist's designation for provitamin D, she would probably buy two on the principle that whatever contains vitamins is O.K. As the fellow said, "What's in a name?" Perhaps a great deal. All these unfamiliar and unpronounceable names must be listed on food labels by law, although they may do little to enlighten the consumer. After spending hours in markets reading lists of ingredients, I can bear witness that the labels do read like a chemistry textbook, and that it would take a professional chemist to interpret them. But does that mean that these unpronounceables are inherently bad?

Not being chemists, most purchasers must rely on faith, on enforcing agencies such as the Food and Drug Administra-

Figure 7. Collage of labels from various prepared
foods

tion and the Department of Agriculture, and on the reputation of the manufacturer.

New foods with new ingredients are constantly being added
to market shelves, but many similar chemicals are used again
and again. Monosodium glutamate (MSG), for example, can
be found in hundreds of food items. It is in my aim in this
chapter to make a number of these strange sounding additives
more familiar so that they will appear less frightening.

After a great deal of debate Congress finally arrived at the
following defintion of a food additive:

> The term "food additive" means any substance the intended
> use of which results or may reasonably be expected to result,
> directly or indirectly, in its becoming a component or other-
> wise affecting the characteristics of any food (including any
> substance intended for use in producing, manufacturing, pack-

ing, processing, preparing, treating, packaging, transporting or holding food: and including any source of radiation intended for such use), if such substance is not generally recognized, among experts qualified by scientific training and experience to evaluate its safety, as having been adequately shown through scientific procedures (or, in the case of a substance used in food prior to January 1, 1958, through either scientific procedures or experience based on common use in food) to be safe under the conditions of its intended use. . . .

With this definition firmly impressed, it may also be helpful to our discussion to note that the Food Protection Committee of the National Research Council, National Academy of Sciences, has stated in their publication, *The Use of Chemical Additives in Food Processing*,* some of the justifiable uses of food additives. Whereas these definitions are not legally binding, they are recommendations of the highest order.

(1) maintenance of nutritional quality, for example by use of antioxidants

(2) enhancement of keeping quality or stability with a resulting reduction in food wastage, through the use of antioxidants, antimicrobial agents, inert gases, meat cures, etc.

(3) enhancement of attractiveness by means of coloring and flavoring agents, emulsifiers, stabilizers, thickeners, clarifiers, and bleaching agents. (Food that appeals to the eye as well as to the palate is not a whim of the food producers; it is a need recognized by all nutritionists, because proteins, vitamins, and minerals serve no purpose unless they are eaten.)

(4) providing essential aids in food processing. (These include acids, alkalis, buffers, sequestrants, and various other types of chemicals.)

---

*Number 1274, 1965.

Considering the fact that food additives are useful and indeed necessary to feed the world's millions, the Food and Agriculture Organization and the World Health Organization of the United Nations have issued a set of recommendations about the use of intentional food additives.

These are as follows:

(1) A food additive should be technologically effective.

(2) A food additive should be safe in use.

(3) A food additive should not be used in any greater quantity than is necessary to achieve the effect stipulated.

(4) A food additive should never be used with the intention of misleading the consumer as to the nature and quality of food.

(5) The use of nonnutrient food additives should be kept to the practicable minimum.

The U. N. Organizations also noted that the use of chemicals in foods is not in the best interests of the consumer if they are used:

(1) to disguise the results of faulty processing and handling

(2) to deceive the customer

(3) when the result is a substantial reduction of the nutritive value of the food

(4) when the chemical effect can be obtained by food manufacturing processes which are economically feasible.

The admittedly extreme examples below demonstrate the extent to which additives may be used in foods available today:

General Foods' Dream Whip (a whipped topping mix) contains eleven ingredients including sugar (a sweetener), hydrogenated vegetable oils (shortening), BHA, or butylated hydroxyanisole (an antioxidant), propylene glycol monostearate (an emulsifier), lactose (for a caramel flavor), sodium caseinate (a binder), whey solids (texture), sodium silico aluminate (an anticaking agent), hydroxylated lecithin (an emulsifier), and artificial flavor and color.

General Foods' Tang (a synthetic powdered orange drink) contains gum arabic (stabilizer), calcium phosphate (sequestrant), and sodium citrate (acidulant).

Carnation's Instant Breakfast contains sodium silico aluminate (anticaking agent), sodium ascorbate (preservative and color fixative), ammonium carrageenan (for thickening and stabilizing), basic copper carbonate (nutrient supplement), ferric orthophosphate (nutrient supplement), and pyridoxine hydrochloride (nutrient supplement).

Jello 1-2-3 Orange Flavored Dessert Mix contains adipic acid (an acidulant), polyglycol esters of fatty acids (emulsifiers), guar gum (thickener), sodium citrate (buffer), BHA (an antioxidant), and fumaric acid (an acidulant).

If additives were removed from these foods, they would simply cease to exist. The same would be true of hundreds of other food products including all frozen cream cakes, eclairs, and cheesecakes whose shelf life would simply become too limited to allow them to be commercially produced.

In addition to the types of additives we shall treat in this chapter, a broad spectrum of other chemicals are used by food processors. Some prevent the sprouting of potatoes in storage; others hasten the ripening of honeydew melons and bananas; still others accelerate the curing of meats and the bleaching and aging of flour. There are many more.

What follows is a consideration of the general categories of additives most frequently encountered by dedicated label readers.

· **Preservatives** ·

Preservatives are chemicals added to food formulations to inhibit or prevent the growth of microbes. The type of preservative will depend on the food product and the species of microbe involved; microbes are almost as finicky in their food preferences as you or I.

Preservatives of one type or another are man's oldest food additive. For thousands of years smoking has contributed many chemical preservatives according to the different types of wood used, while relatively more recently Herodotus noted that the Egyptians ate many kinds of fish that had been preserved by salt.

Most foods are subject to attack by molds, bacteria, and yeast. The degree of susceptibility depends on the item's moisture content. Cereal grains, nuts, and seeds, for example, are inherently so low in moisture that they do not need preservatives. They are too dry to allow the growth of any type of microbe, and they can be stored for years without spoiling.

Root vegetables, potatoes, flour, dried fruits, apples, fats, and butter will keep for a month or two, perhaps three, because their moisture content is low—but not as low as the seeds. Then there are the foods with a high moisture content that will not keep at all without benefit of low temperatures or the assistance of chemicals. Thus the simple definition of a chemical preservative is anything added to prevent spoilage. This includes sugar, which in high concentration such as is found in jam or jelly acts in such a way as to make the moisture unavailable to most bacteria.

Whereas the heat of baking destroys the microbes present in flour and other ingredients used to make bread and cakes, baked goods are exposed to microorganisms in the air both before and after wrapping; the packaging is not intended to be airtight. Preservatives retard the rapid proliferation of mold. The chemical preservatives most frequently listed on the labels of baked goods are calcium and sodium propionate. Calcium propionate is usually preferred in bread products to increase the content of calcium and to avoid the possibility of depressing gas formation by yeast. The sodium and potassium propionates are more frequently used in cakes where leavening is accomplished chemically.

Often sodium diacetate and lactic acid are also added to inhibit "ropiness" in bread. Rope is a bacterial contamination that occurs in hot and humid weather. It can be identified by the interesting odor of overripe pineapples or strawberries, discolored crust and crumbs, and gummy dough. The bacteria producing "ropiness" are found in soil and dust and can easily find their way into the dough.

Sorbic acid and its sodium or potassium salts * are extensively used to prevent or retard mold growth in bread (see Figures 8 and 9), cheese, syrups, pie fillings, jams, mayonnaise, fruit juices, and a variety of other products. They are also used in many pickle products to prevent the growth of yeasts. Several representative commercial foods containing these preservatives are A & P's Mel-O-Bit Pasteurized Process Pimento Cheese (sorbic acid); A & P's Frozen Cream Cheese Cake and Sara Lee's Frozen Blueberry Cream Cheese Cake, A & P's Dark Chocolate Fudge Frosting Mix (potassium

---

*Although they are often called "sorbates," they should not be confused with the polysorbates 60 and 80, which are emulsifying agents.

Figure 8. Mold on bread

Figure 9. Bread mold, magnified many times

sorbate); Milani's Low-Calorie French Lady Dressing (sorbic acid). Di-Et Imitation Pasteurized Process Cheese Spread uses sodium propionate as a preservative as do Arnold's Dutch Boy Sandwich Buns.

The chemical preservatives with the longest histories of use in food and beverages are benzoic acid and its sodium analog, sodium benzoate. It is difficult to find a carbonated beverage, orange drink, apple cider, or fruit cocktail whose label doesn't say "$\frac{1}{10}$ of 1 percent sodium benzoate added as preservative." High acidity is common to all these products, and it is in this environment that the benzoates are most effective as preservatives. Maraschino cherries usually also contain sodium benzoate, as do margarine and many of the newer low-calorie items such as Mayonette, a low-calorie imitation mayonnaise. Prepared béarnaise and hollandaise sauces also usually contain a form of benzoate.

Another particularly interesting chemical known to chemists as a chelating agent (from the Greek, *chelae* = claw) has several uses as a food additive depending on its concentration, the specific food in which it is used, and the other chemicals present. This one is calcium disodium EDTA, short for *e*thylene*d*iamine *t*etracetic *a*cid. It is one of the ingredients of salad dressings such as Bonique's Red Wine Vinegar and Oil Dressing as well as of Mayonette Low Calorie Imitation Mayonnaise previously noted. Best Foods uses it in their Fanning's Bread and Butter Pickles as both a preservative and a flavor enhancer. (See page 99 for a fuller discussion of chelating agents.)

Sulfur dioxide has been used for centuries as a food pre-servative. Sulfur dioxide is usually discussed along with the sulfites, sodium sulfite, potassium sulfite, sodium bisulfite, and others. All of them appear to work best in highly acid products. For example, $\frac{1}{30}$ percent of sodium bisulfite helps in the preservation of Realemon's Lemon Juice. The sulfites are generally used as dry salts that are easily dissolved in water to form sulfurous acid. This accounts for their use as a preservative in such products as Keebler's Wheat Toast crackers, French's Instant Mashed Potatoes, and a great variety of cookies.

With the spread of refrigeration and the development of dehydrated foods, chemical preservation is required more and more infrequently.

· **Sweeteners** ·

Ever since man tasted honey, he has liked sweet-tasting foods. Until the late 19th century, the desire for a sweet taste was satisfied primarily by sugar. Although over a hundred substances are classified chemically as "sugars," only one is by common usage called *sugar*. This is the natural sweetener sucrose ($C_{12}H_{22}O_{11}$), obtained in crystalline form from both sugar cane and sugar beets. (Sucrose is also the sweetening agent in maple syrup.) To the chemist, sucrose is a disaccharide * and, consequently, a carbohydrate.

Sugar's chemical and physical properties have made it the world's most widely used sweetener, as well as one of the most versatile ingredients in food preparation. It contributes body to a variety of beverages, and tenderness to baked goods through peptization of proteins, color when caramelized, and in sufficient quantities it is an effective preservative. Consequently the food industry uses 7 million tons of sugar an-

---

*Its molecule consists of one unit each of the monosaccharides glucose and fructose.

nually in bakery products and cereals, confections, ice cream and dairy products, beverages, jams, jellies, frozen and canned foods, and many other products. According to the U.S. Department of Agriculture, annual per capita consumption of sugar in the U.S. has been holding fairly steady at 97 pounds. And we are not the biggest users, as some may think. Table 4 compares the average annual consumption of eleven countries around the world.

TABLE 4
ANNUAL PER CAPITA SUGAR CONSUMPTION (in pounds)

Ireland	127
Holland	120
England	110
Denmark	110
New Zealand	107
United States	97
Portugal	12
Pakistan	8
Congo	6
North Korea	4
Nigeria	3
Average (world)	38

Refined sugar is pure carbohydrate, containing no fats, proteins, or vitamins, and it has the food value of all carbohydrates—4 calories per gram, 120 calories per ounce, or 1920 calories per pound. A teaspoon or a lump of sugar contains 18 calories, so the person who takes two lumps in his tea or coffee and drinks half a dozen cups a day is absorbing 168 calories from sugar alone, or about 10 percent of his day's caloric intake.

It was this kind of steep escalation that led to the explosion in consumption of nonnutritive, or more properly noncaloric, sweeteners in the early 1960's. Interestingly enough,

'*This sugar substitute is perfect except for one thing.
It's salty.*'

Figure 10

in this instance the widespread weight consciousness of the
public did not drive chemists to develop suitable products.
The products were already waiting.

Constantin Fahlberg, a German organic chemist, accidentally discovered the first artificial noncaloric sweetener
while working at Johns Hopkins University during the summer of 1879. He was studying the oxidation of derivatives
of toluene when some of the compound spattered on his
fingers. Contrary to good laboratory practice, he licked his
fingers and was surprised by the sweetness of what he tasted.
The Princes of Serendip * could not have been more surprised.
Fahlberg had discovered saccharin, and it was introduced
commercially in 1900.

---

*Horace or Horatio Walpole, the Fourth Earl of Oxford, coined the term
serendipity in his novel *The Three Princes of Serendip*, written in 1754.
In it he told of the happy adventures of three men who just couldn't miss
stumbling onto the most marvelous things when they weren't looking
for them.

As if to prove that serendipity stalks chemistry laboratories, Michael Sveda, a graduate student at the University of Illinois, accidentally discovered the sweetness of cyclohexylsulfamic acid half a century later. In 1937, Sveda was studying the ability of sulfamide derivatives to inhibit bacteria. Legend has it that, being an inveterate chewer of cigarettes, he brushed a ribbon of tobacco from his lips, and inadvertently tasted the sweetness of the chemicals he was working with. However, it wasn't until 1950 that Sucaryl (calcium cyclamate) was made available to the public.

Saccharin is an odorless, white crystalline powder sparingly

TABLE 5
RELATIVE POWER OF SWEETENERS

Sugar or Sugar Product	Sweetness Value
Sucrose	100
Fructose	140–175
Invert sugar	100–130
Glucose	70–75
Corn syrup	60
Maltose	30
Lactose (milk sugar)	15
Sucrose	1
Cyclamate	30
Saccharin	300–500

soluble in water. Having had a long history of safe use, it is not considered a food additive. Although it has 300 to 500 times the sweetness of sucrose, to which all sweetners are compared (see Table 5), saccharin is particularly bitter unless greatly diluted.* This is why it can be used in such small quantities.

The second of the two most extensively used noncaloric

*In order to make it completely water soluble, saccharin is treated with sodium hydroxide to produce sodium saccharin.

sweeteners are the cyclamates. Both the sodium and the calcium salts are white, crystalline, odorless powders. However, calcium cyclamate is the preferred compound for people on sodium-free diets. Whereas they are only one-tenth as sweet as saccharine, many people believe the cyclamates have a less disagreeable aftertaste.

Sugar has the ability to impart density or "mouthfeel" to soft drinks which artificial sweeteners cannot do. So bodying agents must be added to beverages made from synthetics to avoid a "watery" taste. Thus one of a variety of gums—carrageenan, arabic, algin, or carboxymethylcellulose (CMC) —are often listed on the labels of diet beverages.

Cyclamates were considered safe until tests revealed gross abnormalities in chick embryos that developed from eggs into which cyclamate had been injected. In other experiments rats fed massive doses of cyclamates developed bladder cancers. As a result, on October 21, 1969, the Food and Drug Administration ordered all production of general purpose products containing cyclamates to cease. It further decreed that by January 1, 1970, all beverages using the product, including packaged mixes, must be removed from market shelves.

Although there is no indication that human bladder cancer is on the increase, or that the effect of cyclamates in rats can be related to man, the FDA acted on the authority of the Delaney clause, which specifies that a chemical found toxic to animals cannot be used for human consumption.

By the middle of June, 1970, the FDA issued a statement indicating that cyclamates might not be as hazardous as previously thought, and that they would be restudied.

The demand for low or noncaloric sweeteners has led to research for a cyclamate substitute. Two possibilities currently being tested for safety are the dihydrochalcones and the aspartylphenylalanine methyl esters.

Dihydrochalcones are derived from bitter-tasting substances called flavonoids or flavanone glycosides found in oranges, lemons, and grapefruits. Department of Agriculture researchers have recently found these flavonoids could be chemically modified to convert the bitterness to sweetness. They worked with the flavonoids narangen (from grapefruit peels), neohesperidin (from the peels of Seville oranges), and hesperidin glucoside (from the peel of sweet oranges). Neohesperidin dihydrochalcone is reported to be 1500 times sweeter than sucrose—which would make it five times sweeter than saccharin and fifty times sweeter than the cyclamates. Naragen dihydrochalcone, though not as sweet, is still one hundred times sweeter than sucrose. Until the safety evaluation trials are completed, it would be premature to consider the flavonoids as potential substitutes. Furthermore, a prohibitive amount of grapefruit peel may be needed to supply the anticipated demand for the artificial sweeteners derived from it.

Aspartylphenylalanine methyl ester is not dependent on limited natural resources. Its discovery was another laboratory "accident." APME is a linking of the amino acids phenylalanine and aspartic acid, which occur naturally in many plants and animals. Neither of the acids are sweet to the taste by themselves, but when they are combined the result is reported to be one hundred times as sweet as sucrose and without an aftertaste, which speaks well for it.

• Flavoring (flavor enhancers or potentiators) •

For hundreds of years flavor secrets have been handed down within families. The "unique" ingredients added to food and drink to make them distinct or outstanding have been closely guarded "secrets."

For example, the label on the back of Prince Charles
Edward's Liqueur, Drambuie, states:

> The origin of Drambuie forms a direct link with one of
> the most romantic episodes in the history of Great Britain.
> When Prince Charlie came to Scotland in 1745 to make his
> gallant but unsuccessful attempt to regain the throne of his
> ancestors, he presented the recipe of his personal liqueur to
> a Mackinnon of Skye as a reward for his services. The secret
> of its preparation has ever since remained with the Mac-
> kinnon family, and the manufacture has been carried on by
> successive generations to this day. Drambuie is a pleasing
> liqueur, unique in its flavour, and highly esteemed for its
> exquisite delicacy of bouquet.

Only recently have chemists and physiologists begun to
understand the elements that come together to make up flavor
and the perception of flavor. For example, we now know
that the very distinctive taste (and odor) of garlic is due
to the naturally occurring chemical, allyl isothiocyanate. Although historians tell us that the French crusaders in Con-
stantinople revolted the natives with their "garlic breath," I
doubt that the Turks would have been comforted had they
known the chemical name of the culprit.

In fifteenth-century Europe spices were not simply a way
to add a whiff of individuality to food. Difficulties of transport and the absence of refrigeration meant that most meat,
fish, and poultry eaten in the Renaissance were either heavily
salted or spoiled; spices were needed simply to make food
edible. Accordingly, one might say that the early spice traders
were the forerunners of the flavoring industry.

There is much we still do not know, but it has been established that flavor is a combination of taste, feeling, and odor
on receptors (taste buds) in the mouth and nose. We also
know that there are only four basic tastes, sweet, sour, salty,

and bitter, and that they are perceived in specific areas of the tongue: the tip is most sensitive to sweet tastes, the sides to sour and salty tastes, and the back to bitter tastes. But obviously there is more to flavor than we now know. If not, there would be little difference between apple pie and chicken salad.

The addition of a flavoring to a food can supply a taste where little or none existed, or it can intensify, modify, or mask an existing flavor. A single substance such as sugar, for example, can do several of these things. Sugar in coffee sweetens the brew, masks the bitterness, and modifies the flavor.

The largest single category of flavorings used in foods are the essential oils. Although the name "essential oil" is relatively new, the use of these oils is not. Before Christ first appeared in Jerusalem, the Chinese were using oil (or attar) of rose.* Since then chemists have synthesized the following *flavors* in the laboratory: amyl acetate for banana, allyl caproate for pineapple, anethole for anise (licorice), carvone for a mint or spicy flavor, cinnamaldehyde for cinnamon, ethyl pelargonate for brandy, alpha ionone for raspberry, phenylethyl isovalerate for peach, and vanillin for vanilla.

In many instances both a natural and a synthetic flavoring are available (see Tables 6 and 7). Because the synthetic is so like the natural product, it is often preferred because it is cheaper, its quality is constant, and it is available year round. Supplies of the natural product can be shut off without

---

*It may be saddening to some to learn how far chemists have gone. One of the major ingredients that give roses their unique odor is phenylethyl alcohol, now available in bulk for a small price.

TABLE 6
SYNTHETIC FLAVORING AGENTS

Chemical Name	Flavor Contributed	Use
Acetanisole	Sharp—slight haylike	Brown and nutty flavors
Acetophenone	Pungent, hay	Fruity
C_9-Nonyl aldehyde	Sharp orange, floral	Citrus—orange, lemon
C_{11}-Undecyl aldehyde	Sharp citrus orange	Orange citrus
Allyl caproate	Pineapple, fruity	Fruity and tutti-frutti
Allyl disulfide	Sharp garlic	Onion, garlic
Allyl isothiocyanate	Sharp—mustard oil	Synthetic mustard
Amyl propionate	Estery, pineapple	Fruity flavors, liquors
Anisic alcohol	Sweet, peach	Apricot, peach flavors
Benzyl acetate	Synthetic jasmine	Fruity flavor
Benzyl isoeugenol	Slight spicy	Clove, spicy
Ethyl caproate	Fruity, sharp, pungent	Imitation fruits, (pineapple)
Ethyl pelargonate	Fruity, brandy	Alcoholic beverage flavors
Ethyl phenylacetate	Honey	Honey flavor
Ethyl vanillin	Vanilla	Chocolate and vanilla flavors
Linalool	Light floral	Citrus, carbonated beverages
Methyl Anthranilate	Orange, neroli	Grape
Phenylethyl acetate	Rose, sweet	Berry flavor, caramel, honey
Phenylethyl isovalerate	Fruity	Heavy fruity (peach, etc.)
Rhodinol	Rosy	Oriental candy, ginger ale
Yara yara	Acacia orange	Citrus, orange

TABLE 7
NATURAL FLAVORING AGENTS

Name	Chemical Component Eliciting Flavor	Flavor Contributed	Use
Anise	Anethole	Anise	Licorice-anise flavor
Basil	Methyl chavicol, cineole, linalool	Medicinal, herby, slight licorice	Spicy flavors, meat products
Bergamot	Limonene	Bitter orange	Citrus flavor, orange, cola
Betula	Methyl salicylate	Wintergreen	Mint-type flavors
Caraway	d-Carvone	Caraway	Spice flavor, bakery products
Cardamom	Terpineol, cineole	Spicy, slight lemon citrus	Processed meats
Cassia	Cinnamic aldehyde	Cinnamon, bite	Hot, spicy, candy, bakery products
Celery Seed	Limonene, sedenene	Celery, spicy	Spice blends, carbonated beverages, meat products
Chamomile		Pungent aromatic	Liqueur flavor
Cinnamon	Cinnamic aldehyde	Spicy, hot	Spice flavors, cola beverages
Clove	Eugenol	Warm, pungent, spicy clove	Spice and medicinal flavors, meat products
Copaiba	Caryophyllene	Bitter balsamic	Medicinal flavor
Coriander	d-Linalool	Spicy	General spice flavors, meats
Dill (weed)	Phellandrene, carvone	Herby, bitter	Pickle spice flavors
Fennel	Anethole	Anise	Liqueur, salad dressing

TABLE 7
NATURAL FLAVORING AGENTS

Name	Chemical Component Eliciting Flavor	Flavor Contributed	Use
Grapefruit	Limonene	Grapefruit	Citric products (beverages)
Hops	Humulone	Fatty, green, oily	Beverage flavors
Horseradish	Allyl isothiocyanate	Hot, bite, penetrating	Hot sauces
Lavandin	Linalyl acetate	Pungent lavender	Dentrifices, chewing gum
Mace	d-Pinene, myristicin, d-Camphene	Nutmeg, aromatic, pine	Spice flavors
Marjoram	Terpinene	Spicy, pungent	Spice flavors
Mustard	Allyl isothiocyanate	Pungent, sharp	Relish flavors, salad dressings
Nutmeg	Pinene, myristicin	Spicy, hot, nutmeg	General spice flavors, baked goods
Orris root	Methyl ionone	Violet	Raspberry flavors
Patchouly		Earthy, slight woody	Cola beverages
Pepper	Piperidine	Warm, spicy	General spice flavors, prepared meats
Rosemary	Pinene, borneol, cineole	Slight medicinal, woody	Herb blends, mouthwashes
Sage	Thujone	Spicy, warm, tea-like	Meat flavors, poultry
Thyme	Thymol	Medicinal, burnt	Medicinal flavors
Ylang ylang	Benzyl alcohol, linalool, cresol methyl ether	Fragrant, slight orange	Beverage flavors

adequate notice as a result of political relationships between countries or crises within one. Moreover, the natural product can vary in its chemical composition from year to year depending upon climate and fertilizer.

The best known and most widely used flavor enhancer is MSG. It was first prepared in a chemical laboratory in Germany in 1867, but it wasn't until 1908 that Kikunae Ikeda, a Japanese chemist at the University of Tokyo, discovered its flavor-enhancing properties. Ikeda had been trying to learn what there was in certain Japanese seaweed that affected the flavor of foods to which it was added. He discovered that the "secret" ingredient is MSG and that it has an unusual ability to intensify the flavor of many meat, fish, or poultry dishes—all high in protein. Moreover, whereas MSG has the ability to enhance the flavor of many foods, it does not add any flavor of its own. It is this quality which distinguishes an enhancer from a seasoning.

MSG is still generally recognized as safe (see Chapter 4), but it is currently being reevaluated as a result of several animal studies and the belief that it is responsible for the "Chinese Restaurant Syndrome." In October, 1969, Dr. John W. Olney of Washington University Medical School in St. Louis, claimed that he had produced brain damage in infant mice by injecting them with MSG. He also reported that one rhesus monkey injected with MSG incurred similar damage. As a result he asked that MSG be removed from baby foods. Pending additional research, the major baby food manufacturers are acceding to this suggestion.

Not much MSG is needed to enhance the flavor of foods, but only infinitesimal amounts of another class of chemicals, known as flavor potentiators, are needed to do the same job.

Interestingly enough Dr. Shintara Kodama, a colleague of Dr. Ikeda, discovered the potentiators.

Potentiators (or 5′ [5 prime] nucleotides, as they are designated chemically) are known to intensify the flavor of meats, fish, cereals, nuts, and fruits, and three of them are found in well-known products. Disodium inosinate and disodium guanylate, for example, are listed among the many ingredients of Lipton's and Knorr's prepared soup mixes as well as Chung King's chicken chow mein. Ethyl maltol has been much used in soft drinks, jams, gelatins, and most recently in instant breakfast food mixes like Carnation, Sego, and Metrecal.

These three potentiators have been cleared for use in food by the Food and Drug Administration, and are listed as permitted food additives.

• Coloring Agents •

Before we take the first mouthful of any food we unconsciously note its color to see whether it falls within an acceptable range. Almost instantaneously the brain returns the message: eat, or don't eat.

For example, when bread and rolls were experimentally baked from flour containing a significant amount of algal protein, the resulting green products were uniformly rejected. Green bread is too far removed from most people's subjective image of what bread ought to look like. Similarly yellow meat and blue potatoes would find few takers.

Coloring agents (or colorants) are added to soft drinks, cheese, butter, ice cream, cake mixes, breakfast cereals, candies, sausages, canned meats, puddings, and many other foods,

because in the manufacturing process many foods (or ingredients) change color to a degree that would be unacceptable to the consumer. The added color restores the finished
item to a familar color range.

On the other hand, colorants can also be used to conceal
damaged or inferior products. For example, it is well known
that oranges ripen before the skin turns completely orange.
Few will object if the processor adds orange color to make
them more attractive. But the addition of orange color to
unripe or green oranges would meet strong resistance. Realizing that mature, tree-ripened oranges are often streaked with
brown, the Food and Drug Administration permits processors
to color them, but only if they are ripe, of acceptable quality,
and stamped "color added" or "artificially colored."

It is of prime importance to note that every colorant used
in foods must be certified by the FDA prior to use. The unde-
clared addition of any color is a violation of both state and
federal laws.

In 1960, Congress placed natural as well as synthetic colors
under a single law. Before that time only synthetic colors
had been subject to a federal program of pretesting and
certification of batches of dyes.

Cochineal, a rich crimson or scarlet dye widely used in
meat products, beverages, confectionary items, baked goods,
and spices is still obtained from *Coccus cacti*, an insect that
makes its home on a certain variety of cactus found in the
Canary Islands and South America. However, it should be
borne in mind that, although the dye is obtained from the
dried bodies of the insects, it is actually the extracted carminic
acid, with the unbearable technical name of methyl tetra-o-
methylcarminate that is responsible for the coloring property.

Turmeric (*Curcuma longa*), from the root of an East Indian

herb of the ginger family, has long been used as a spice. It is also capable of contributing an intense yellow dye (in fact an oleoresin *) used in meat products and prepared French-type salad dressings.

Annatto has long been used to deepen the yellow color of butter and margarine and to impart the yellow-to-peach range of color to cheese, bakery products, beverages, ice cream, cake mixes, breakfast cereals, and edible oils. It is obtained from the pulp surrounding the seeds of the tropical annatto tree, *Bixa orellana*. The active ingredients are bixin or nor-bixin, both carotenoid-like compounds, but annatto has been found to have greater stability and five times the coloring power of an equal amount of carotene.

Yet another natural yellow-to-orange dye is obtained from the dried stigmas of the American saffron or safflower, *Crocus sativus*. It has long been used to color a variety of meat products.

William Perkins, a young chemistry student, made the first synthetic dye, a mauve color, in 1856. Other colors were soon synthesized in European laboratories, and by 1900 some eighty synthetic dyes were being used in foods. To be sure many of them belonged only in cloth and certainly not in food. By 1906 Congress passed a food and drug act (often called the Pure Food Law) that permitted only seven dyes to be used in foods. Currently ten synthetic water-soluble dyes are approved for addition to foods. Among these are two blues, a green, three reds, a violet, and two yellows.

Synthetic dyes now account for about 90 percent of all colorants used in foods. The synthetics provide a greater in-

---

*Oleoresins belong to a class of chemicals whose molecular configuration consists of an essential oil and a resin.

tensity of color; they are more stable and more uniform because their production can be controlled, and they are less expensive. Nevertheless, the natural colors are still used because in certain cases none of the certified synthetics will do.

·   **Leavening Agents**   ·

We are all familiar with the story of the exodus of the Israelites from Egypt and how, in their haste to leave, they were unable to take the leavening needed to produce bread. As a result, their dough did not rise and their "bread," which they called matzo, was flat and hard. Since that time, Jewish people celebrate their Passover holiday by eating only un-leavened bread.

A leavening agent is any chemical or biologic substance that can produce bubbles of gas in dough. The heat of baking makes the bubbles expand so that the dough rises. As the heat increases, the protein in the flour, milk, and eggs undergoes a change in molecular structure called denaturation. In this case the denatured proteins form rigid cells around the bubbles, thereby preventing the collapse of the dough on cooling.

The three major leavening agents are air, carbon dioxide, and steam. Carbon dioxide is formed as a result of the multi-plication of bacteria or yeast cells, or from the chemical reaction of baking powder with the moisture of the dough. Air can be beaten into egg whites or incorporated by creaming fat and sugar. Steam, of course, is formed when the moisture in dough is heated to the point at which it changes from a liquid to a gas.

Before the chemical action of leavening was understood, two types of microorganisms, yeast and bacteria, were used almost exclusively to obtain the gas necessary to make the dough rise so that the resulting baked goods would have the desired texture.

Dough contains glucose, a carbohydrate sugar. In the presence of yeast cells, which utilize or metabolize sugar, carbon dioxide and ethyl alcohol are produced as end products. The chemical reaction is

$$C_6H_{12}O_6 \longrightarrow 2C_2H_5OH + 2CO_2$$

glucose   yeast   ethyl   carbon dioxide
                      alcohol

The carbon dioxide is the gas that promotes leavening or rising, whereas the ethyl alcohol, part of the pleasant odor emanating from bakeries and kitchens, evaporates in the heat of baking. Although a number of recipes call for using sucrose, a disaccharide sugar, the chemical reaction is much the same once the sucrose is converted to glucose by yeast enzymes.

Because yeast can be an unreliable source of gas and because the demand for bread and cakes is so great, chemical baking powders have all but replaced yeast as the preferred leavening agents.

Baking powders are generally composed of sodium bicarbonate (baking soda), an acid salt such as calcium mono- (or dibasic) phosphate and starch. The starch helps keep the ingredients dry and nonreactive, so that a given volume of baking powder will create a given amount of gas. The phosphate and the bicarbonate readily react in the presence of water to produce carbon dioxide.

In the double-action type of baking powders, little or no carbon dioxide is formed at room temperature. This is because the sodium aluminum sulfate that has been added suppresses gas formation until oven temperatures are reached.

In this way none of the gas is wasted between the time of mixing and baking.* Rarely will you see a label bearing the ingredient sodium aluminum sulfate (SAS) without the accompanying calcium phosphate. If SAS were used alone the bitter byproduct sodium sulfate would result. Interestingly enough, when SAS baking powders first appeared there was considerable concern that aluminum could be poisonous. Today that's only a fading memory.

In grandmother's day, "spirits of hart's horn" was used as a leavening for cookies. Actually, she was in effect using ammonium bicarbonate, which is still called for today to improve the volume of cream puffs and eclairs. Morton's Frozen Coconut Cream Pie and Frozen Chocolate Eclairs contain ammonium carbonate, $(NH_4)_2CO_3$, for rapid leavening.

Baking soda, a long-time standard used by generations of bakers, is sodium bicarbonate, $NaHCO_3$. It will react with an acid to form carbon dioxide and water. In many older recipes the acids involved are the lactic acid present in milk, the acetic acid present in vinegar, or other organic acids naturally present in the food. In the case of lactic acid, the reaction is

$$NaHCO_3 + C_3H_6O_3 \rightarrow NaC_3H_5O_3 + CO_2 + H_2O$$

A major disadvantage of using baking soda alone is the

---

*This permits the refrigeration of a dough prepared on one day and baking a day or two later without loss of leavening capacity. At room temperature sodium aluminum sulfate (SAS) decomposes slowly to form sodium sulfate and hydrated aluminum sulfate as follows:

$$Na_2SO_4 \cdot Al_2(SO_4)_3 \cdot 24H_2O \rightarrow NA_2SO_4 + Al_2(SO_4)_3 \cdot 24H_2O$$

This is followed by the decomposition of the aluminum hydrate simultaneously with the reaction between the calcium phosphate and sodium bicarbonate:

$$Al_2(SO_4)_3 + 12H_2O \rightarrow 2[Al(H_2O)_5OH]^{2+} + 2H^+ + 3SO_4^{2-}$$
$$3CaHPO_4 + 2NaHCO_3 \rightarrow Ca_3(PO_4)_2 + Na_2HPO_4 + 2CO_2 + 2H_2O$$

tremendous variation in the amounts of acid naturally present in foods. Should too little acid be present, as it often is, the dough will not rise and the results will resemble what the Israelites "brought forth from Egypt." The reaction in this instance will be primarily

$$2NaHCO_3 \rightarrow Na_2CO_3 + H_2O + CO_2$$

with sodium carbonate as an undesirable end product. Sodium carbonate, as distinct from the bicarbonate, has a strong, soapy, bitter taste; it can make the resulting product crumbly, and it can, on reaction with the carbohydrates, produce brown spots in the finished product.

Potassium acid tartrate, or cream of tartar,* is the essential ingredient of tartrate baking powders, and has been used for several centuries. The tartrate powders react rapidly—as soon as water is added CO_2 is released. Thus one must work quickly between mixing and baking in order not to lose the available gas.

To produce the many types of preleavened mixes for cakes, biscuits, muffins, rolls, and pancakes, special combinations of baking powders are used to produce the desired results.

• Stabilizers and Thickeners •

For centuries certain gums extracted from trees and seeds, and certain seaweeds have been used to thicken prepared foods or to stabilize them by binding together the solids and the liquids so that they do not separate.

---

*Called cream of tartar because small floating crystals rise to the top of the liquid like cream on milk—when a concentrated hot water solution of the salt is rapidly cooled. In eighteenth-century literature it is referred to as "creamor tartar."

TABLE 8
SOURCES OF GUMS USED IN FOODS

Type of Gum	Botanical Origin	Major Source
Seaweed Extracts:		
Agar	Gelidium species	Japan, U.S.
Algin	Macrocystis pyrifera	U.S., U.K.
	Laminaria species	
Carrageenan	Chondrus chrispus	U.S., U.K.
	Gigartina species	
Furcellaran	Furcellaria fastigiata	Denmark
Tree exudates and extracts:		
Arabic	Acacia senegal	Sudan
Ghatti	Anogeissus latifolia	India
Karaya	Sterculia urens	India
Larch	Larix occidentalia	U.S.
Tragacanth	Astragalus gummifer	Iran
Seed gums:		
Guar	Cyamopsis tetra-gonolobus	India, Pakistan
Locust bean	Ceratonia siliqua	Mediterranean
Cellulose derivatives:		
Carboxymethyl-cellulose	Wood pulp and cotton linters	U.S.
Methylcellulose and hydroxypropyl-methylcellulose		U.S.

Most commercially used stabilizers and thickeners today are pure plant extracts; a smaller number are chemically modified natural products, and a still smaller third group are entirely synthetic.* Table 8 lists the sources of the stabilizers and

*Many of the tree and seed gums are polysaccharides, or members of the starch-cellulose group of carbohydrates. In contrast to the saccharides many of the polysaccharides are not soluble in water and do not have the sweet taste of their smaller-moleculed relations. As many will remember from elementary chemistry, the saccharides do not turn purple-black when iodine is added to them, while the starchy polysaccharides do.

thickeners, while Table 9 breaks down the types of foods they are used in and the role they play.

If stabilizers are not added to chocolate milk, or chocolate drinks, the chocolate particles tend to settle to the bottom. The stabilizer slightly alters the viscosity of the milk and thereby keeps the chocolate in suspension. The addition of a small amount of stabilizer can also prolong the life of the "head" on a glass of beer.

The texture of ice cream and other frozen desserts is dependent, in part, on the size of the ice crystals in the product. Before stabilizers were used, part of the water would freeze into crystals, producing "sandy" or "grainy" ice cream. The added stabilizers now bind up this excess water, preventing its freezing and subsequent crystallization.

Stabilizers are also used to protect the flavoring oils used in many cake, gelatin, and pudding mixes. These oils are highly susceptible to evaporation; in the chemist's terminology they are volatile. An added stabilizer surrounds the thousands of microscopic oil globules, and keeps air from getting to them.

Thickeners are added to icings, cheese spreads, salad dressings, pie fillings, soups, and gravies to provide the desired consistency. Pillsbury, for example, uses both carrageenan and sodium carboxymethylcellulose in its "heat and serve" Cinnamon Rolls with Icing, to achieve two different qualities.

Sugar-sweetened soft drinks have a certain amount of "body." When nonnutritive sweeteners are used instead of sugar, the beverages lose this "body," which must be replaced with additives such as sodium alginate, cellulose gums, and pectins.

To judge by a random selection of foods picked from market shelves, it would appear that carrageenan is the most widely used stabilizer. It is obtained from *Chondrus crispus*,

TABLE 9

THICKENERS, STABILIZERS, AND THEIR USES

Additive	Function	Type of Food
Agar agar	Thickener	Frozen candied sweet potatoes, ice cream, frozen custard, sherbert
Sodium alginate (algins)	Water retainers	Condiments, salad dressing, cake icing, chocolate milk, dessert toppings
Carrageenan	Stabilizer	Chocolate milk, syrups for frozen products, evaporated milk, pressure-dispersed whipped cream, cottage cheese
Sodium carboxymethyl cellulose	Stabilizer, bodying agent	Ice cream, icing for baked goods, cheese spreads, dietetic canned fruit products, fruited ham glaze
Dextrin	Stabilizer	Beer, baked goods, gelatin desserts
Gelatin	Thickener	Fruit gelatins and puddings, cream cheese, cheese spreads, cheese foods
Cellulose gums	Thickener, suspender, bodying agent	Dessert mixes, cake mixes, salad dressing
Gum acacia (gum arabic)	Thickener, stabilizer	Beer, soft drinks, ice cream, imitation fruit juice drinks
Locust bean gum	Thickener, stabilizer	Cream cheese, fruit sherbert, salad dressing
Guar gum	Thickener, stabilizer, binder	Cheese spreads, baked goods, meat products
Gum tragacanth	Thickener	Pickle relish, icings, fruit juices, salad dressings

a species of red algae often called Irish moss, which grows abundantly off the shores of the town of Carrageen on Ireland's northeastern coast.

Extracts of carrageenan were used in the United States as long ago as 1835 for medicinal purposes, but it wasn't until World War II, when Japanese agar became unavailable that dried, purified carrageenan became widely used as a food additive. Its most outstanding property is its high degree of reactivity with proteins, in particular the casein in milk. For this reason only a small quantity need be used to keep the cocoa from settling in chocolate milk. Higher concentrations produce stronger gels such as that obtained in a custard or a flan.

When the surface is broken on certain foods such as chocolate pudding, gelatin fruit puddings, sour cream, and ice cream, the gel tends to contract, forcing out the water which collects in little puddles. Carrageenan is often used to prevent this weeping, or syneresis, as it is called.

"Bulking" and "mouthfeel" are two additional contributions carrageenan can make, and it is widely used to obtain these qualities in soups, sauces, cottage cheese, syrups, and toppings. Pet evaporated milk and Sego, a liquid diet food, are two well-known products using carrageenan. The relatively new instant diet breakfasts, with their long lists of ingredients, use carrageenan to increase viscosity so that settling out of solids does not occur.

Alginic acid and its salts, such as sodium alginate, are also much used in U.S. and European foods. Alginic acid is produced from the giant kelp, *Macrocystis pyrifora*, that grows off the coast of southern California. Our eastern seaboard, particularly around Maine, is rich in another species of kelp, *Laminaria*, which often climbs to a height of 15 feet.

The alginates are used as a gelling agent in such foods as

A & P's Smooth Whip Dessert Topping, ice milk, sherberts, and cheeses, and to keep solids and liquids in suspension in fruit juices.

The widely used thickener gum arabic (also called gum acacia) is obtained from the bark of the acacia trees that grow in hot, dry, high altitudes. Although acacias are found in arid and semi-arid areas around the world, the Sudan is the leading producer of high-grade gum arabic. Its most unusual and useful feature is its high degree of water solubility. As noted earlier, this is the exception rather than the rule for the long chain polysaccharides.

Curiously enough the gum industry is based on an infection. As a response to a microbial invasion of its bark the acacia mobilizes the gum much as an oyster responds to an irritation by producing a pearl. To stimulate gum production the trees are purposely cut to allow bacteria to gain entrance.

Probably the most viscous of all plant gums is tragacanth. It swells so greatly in cold water that it can be used in very small concentrations. It is exuded by the small, thorny *Astragalus* bush that thrives in dry, hilly areas, particularly in the mountains of Turkey and Iran. Tragacanth is found in the form of curled ribbons that become horny on drying, and takes its name from the Greek for "goat's horn": *tragas* = goat and *akantha* = horn.

Because of its high resistance to acids and its ability to form stable emulsions, it is used as a stabilizer in such high-acid foods as salad dressings, pickle relish, and citrus juices.

· **Emulsifiers and Surface Active Agents** ·
Not too long ago to get at the great American snack, peanut butter, you had to get through the oil first. Beyond

it was a gummy glob that was impossible to swallow. The oil and mashed peanuts had to be mixed quite vigorously before the peanut butter was edible. Today this is only a comical memory.

Many homemakers will also recall without nostalgia the time when margarine had to be kneaded in order to prevent leakage of water or separation of the oil from the water-soluble components.

It is the chemical emulsifiers that have made peanut butter, margarine, and many other products instantly usable. The emulsifiers permit the dispersion of tiny globules of one liquid in another. A simple example is oil and water. Shortly after mixing the two together, the oil globules coalesce, rise to the surface, and form a layer over the water. However, with the addition of an emulsifier, the oil and water will mix and stay mixed. (See Table 10.)

TABLE 10
DISPERSE SYSTEMS

Type	Internal Phase	External Phase
Emulsion	Liquid	Liquid
Foam	Gas	Liquid
Aerosol (fog, smoke)	Liquid or solid	Gas
Suspension (sol)	Solid	Liquid

Emulsifiers play important roles in the baking industry. They help to increase volume, uniformity, and fineness of grain, and they make the doughs easier to handle.

Chocolates, or food products coated with chocolate, take on a mottled or cottony look when left at room temperature. The change is caused by a separation of the cocoa butter from the chocolate, and is known to the manufacturers as "bloom." The addition of an emulsifier helps to keep the fat and cocoa butter in a stable relation with the chocolate, so that even at room temperature the chocolate maintains its glossy, lustrous appearance.

Thickening, or increasing the viscosity of foods, can be accomplished by using appropriate stabilizing techniques. For example, the effect of adding oil to mayonnaise is a common but excellent example of an oil-in-water emulsion.

Surface-active agents (or surfactants), of which emulsifiers are one type, are also used to lubricate foods. In this instance lubrication refers to a slipperiness in which the stickiness of caramel or peanut butter, for example, is reduced. Briefly and simply, surfactants are chemicals that alter the surface properties of other materials (foods) they contact. They orient themselves along the boundary of two adjacent surfaces, known as the interface.

In food products, the interface can heat the point of contact between two immiscible liquids (oil-water-mayonnaise), between a liquid and a gas, or between a liquid and a solid.

Surfactants are often classified by the function they serve: stabilizers, emulsifiers, demulsifiers, detergents, foaming or wetting agents, etc.

Among the most widely used emulsifiers are the natural substance lecithin and the synthetic mono- and diglycerides. Lecithin, which is obtained from plant and animal tissue, was used almost exclusively before the advent of the synthetics. However, it cannot fulfill the many functions expected of emulsifiers. You will find lecithin or the glycerides or both listed on hundreds of different food packages. For example, Balsen's Raspberry Cream Wafers and General Foods' Angel Delight Chocolate Dessert Whirl use lecithin. Pillsbury uses mono- and diglycerides in their Hungry Jack mashed potatoes in combination with sodium (or calcium) stearoyl-2-lactylate (a conditioner that increases the strength and volume of the dough). You will find the same combination of chemicals in Jello Whip 'n Chill to keep the ingredients in a stable relationship to one another, and in Betty Crocker's Potato Buds to increase their volume.

The surfactants most widely used in bread, cake, cake mixes, and other baked goods are the mono- and diglycerides. Their primary purposes are to increase volume and improve texture, eating, and keeping qualities. Figure 11 shows photomicrographs of cake batters and the resulting cakes. The air bubbles, which contribute to the volume of the dough, are enclosed in films of protein in which the fat is dispersed.

A & P's Dark Chocolate Flavored Frosting Mix and Betty Crocker's Chocolate Pudding Mix and Sunkist Orange Frosting Mix use mono- and diglycerides to good advantage. More recently General Foods introduced Dream Whip which, according to the advertised photographs of General Foods' cakes, imparts unusual volume and texture. Without the incorporation of propylene glycol monostearate, this would not be possible. Acetylated monoglyceride is one of the ingredients of My-T-Fine Lemon Flavor Pie Filling and Jello's Whip 'n Chill. In addition to emulsifying, these additives also protect the products against loss of moisture. In other foods, mono- and diglycerides impart a better chewing quality depending on their concentration.

Another tongue-twisting additive is glycerol lactopalmitate. Used in A & P's Smooth Whip and Chelten House's Instant Onion Dip, it helps increase aeration during whipping.

Probably the most terrifying sounding of all the surfactant emulsifiers is polyoxyethylene sorbitan monooleate (or tristearate), mercifully shortened to Polysorbate 80. Another family member, Polysorbate 60, is known chemically as

Figure 11. Emulsifiers and their effect on batters and cakes (magnified 100×) **A.** The excellent batter is rather thick and slightly curdled. The air bubbles are coated with fat, and a few dark pools of reserve fat can be seen. The cake has good volume and fine texture.

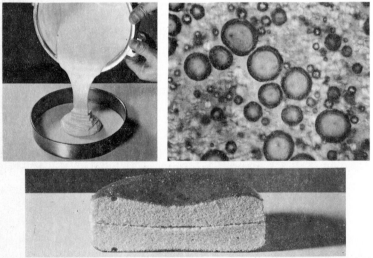

B. This type of emulsifier has promoted the formation of large air bubbles with thick walls. The batter is smooth and viscous with no curdle. But in baking the large bubbles finally burst and the cake falls.

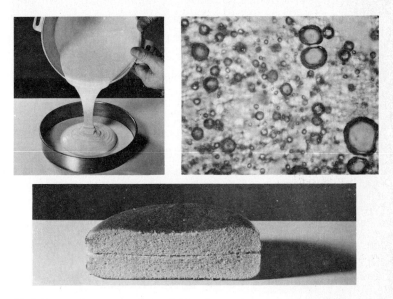

C. Still another type of emulsifier has promoted the formation of small air bubbles with thick walls. The batter is thin and smooth. In the oven the bubbles break, and the resulting cake has a coarse grain and a sunken center.

polyoxyethylene sorbitan monostearate. Both of these Tweens * are included in many products to achieve a smoothness of texture. Polysorbate 80 is found in ice cream, frozen custard, ice milk, sherbet, icings, fillings and toppings, and soft drinks. Polysorbate 60 is used in a variety of cakes and cake mixes and in spray-dried coffee whiteners. In such products as Coffeemate both these emulsifiers are used to speed the dispersion of the "cream." Such items as frozen chocolate eclairs, fruited ham glazes, and Kellogg's Pop Tarts also contain Polysorbate 60. In soft drinks, sherbert, and

*Registered trademark of Atlas Chemical Industries, Inc.

pickles the polysorbates help disperse the essential or flavoring oils that are othewise insoluble in water.

One additional characteristic of surface-active agents is their ability to develop or inhibit foam, depending on their concentration and the other chemicals with which they are combined. Without foam we would have to forego instant mousse mixes, ready-to-eat meringues, and a variety of frostings and pancake mixes. The reverse side of the coin is that certain combinations of food, when moistened and whipped, form unwanted or undesirable foams. Such emulsifiers as the polysorbates and the monoglycerides are able to defoam or prevent the occurrence of foam.

Finally, it is important to bear in mind that a specific emulsifier or surfactant or combination of them is necessary to perform a unique function in a particular food. They must be chosen carefully in order to achieve the desired effect.

· Firming and Anticaking Agents ·

A number of vegetables and fruits tend to soften when they are heated for canning or bottling unless a touch of firming agent has been added. Consequently the canning industry has long put a pinch of calcium salts into peas, potatoes, pickles, cherries, apples, and tomatoes before cooking. This chemical forms a gel with the pectin found in fruits and vegetables and maintains their structural integrity even after cooking. Analysis has shown that the naturally occurring pectin appears to cement the layers of cells together in the raw fruit or vegetable, but that it tends to break down with the heat of cooking, so that fibrous tissues collapse and the food becomes too soft.

The calcium salts are usually added to canned vegetables in the form of calcium chloride,* although citrate and gluconate of calcium are substituted from time to time. Canned apple slices often contain calcium lactate to keep them from becoming too soft.

Most shoppers will recognize the Morton salt trademark: "When it rains, it pours." The Morton people have made a reputation with their immortal message. And to think it was done with just a pinch of sodium silico aluminate!†

To keep salt, sugar, and other powders free-flowing, anticaking substances are added. The American Sugar Company (Domino brand) adds 3 percent of corn starch to its 10X confectioners sugar to keep it from caking, while Hulman and Company, makers of Clabber Girl baking powder, uses both sodium aluminum sulfate and cornstarch to keep its product from absorbing the atmospheric moisture that will cause it to clump and harden.

Look again at the labels of most garlic salts and you will see that calcium stearate has been added. This is an antiwetting agent that prevents the caking to which garlic powder is normally susceptible. General Foods uses the anticaking chemical calcium phosphate to keep its powdered orange drink Tang easily dispersible when water is added.

---

*Calcium chloride is also added to most brands of cottage and cheddar cheese to aid in coagulation during the early stages of cheese making.

†If you can picture granules of salt in the form of tiny blocks, it may be easy to comprehend the role played by the anticaking agent. Salt is deliquescent, that is, it tends to absorb moisture from the air to the extent that its surface becomes wet, producing a film of moisture between the "blocks." When the humidity drops, evaporation of the moisture occurs leaving a weld or bond between the closely packed granules of salt. To prevent this bonding, an anticaking or free-flowing conditioner such as sodium silico aluminate is used. It acts by coating the salt to establish an effective moisture barrier.

The sodium silico aluminate that keeps Morton's salt free flowing is a relatively new additive that shows considerable promise. Consequently it is now used in General Foods' Dream Whip, Jello's Whip 'n Chill, Carnation's Instant Breakfast, Coffeemate (a coffee whitener) and many other dried powders. All of these products must either disperse rapidly or assume the consistency of pudding when water is added.

In addition to sodium silico aluminate (Zeolex) added to table salt, either potassium iodide or cuprous iodide are added to produce an iodized salt. The FDA has approved only these two forms as nutritional iodine sources for human consumption.

Of particular concern to public health authorities is the rising incidence of goiter in recent years. Because the public is relying increasingly upon presalted convenience foods, less iodized salt is being used. As a consequence, goiter, which had all but disappeared in the United States, is once again on the increase.

The thyroid gland is intimately concerned with the concentration and metabolism of iodine to produce two thyroid hormones—thyroxin and triiodothyronine. Note the "iodo" portion, which cleverly indicates the presence of iodine. The production of these two chemicals is absolutely dependent on the presence and utilization of adequate amounts of iodine. These thyroid hormones exert a major influence on human growth and metabolism.

Although thyroid diseases are generally considered in four categories, the underproduction or deficiency of hormone, hypothyroidism, is of greatest concern here. While it is well known that both excessive intake of goitrogens that block iodine synthesis (cf. Chapter 2) or inborn errors of metabolism can induce hypothyroidism, it is most commonly the result of inadequate dietary iodine intake. The fact that goiter is once again prevalent among girls of child-bearing age is cause for alarm because of the direct and well-established relationship between lack of dietary iodine and cretinism. A cretin (from the Swiss-French meaning "poor fellow") is a child dwarfed by a lack of sufficient thyroid secretion during the fetal period. In cretins mental, physical, and sexual development are significantly retarded.

In this instance, then, the added iodine is cast in the role of supplying a nutritional rather than a functional need.

· **Antioxidants** ·

Rancidity is one of the most common types of food spoilage. It is recognizable by an off odor and an off taste caused by oxygen in the air, moisture, heat, or certain enzymes present in many natural fats.

The rate at which fats and oils become rancid on prolonged storage varies with the particular fat and storage conditions. Butter from certain areas of the country, for example, can develop off odors and flavors within days of preparation, while some commercial shortenings can be kept at room temperature for months without developing the slightest odor. For the most part, rancidity is a problem restricted to fatty foods, and the chemical reactions that occur when a fat becomes rancid are of two types, oxidative and hydrolytic.

In the hydrolytic reaction, enzymes speed the reactions of the fat with the other chemical elements of the food to produce foul-smelling fatty acids such as butyric or caproic.

In the oxidative reaction, air (oxygen) adds to the double bonds of some of the unsaturated fats, forming compounds called ketones and aldehydes which are highly odorous.

Reversion * is a milder form of rancidity. It also involves flavor and odor change and usually occurs in vegetable, fish, and certain unsaturated oils. Foods containing large amounts of carbohydrates undergo a different type of oxidation. Rather than developing off odors and tastes, carbohydrates characteristically change color. This is the reaction of various fruits and vegetables that have been sliced and exposed to the air.

Microbial deterioration is one of the most important factors in preserving foods high in carbohydrates and protein, while oxidation is the chief concern with fatty foods.† Curiously enough, vegetable oils, particularly those made from vegetables having seeds, show a distinct resistance to the onset of rancidity. Animal fats, on the other hand, deteriorate fairly rapidly. Some time ago it was shown that resistance to oxidation was related to the presence of chemicals known as antioxidants. These occur naturally in fats and oils, but because the amount present varies with the type of fat or oil, additional antioxidants are often supplied during processing.

The added antioxidants prevent or retard rancidity and reversion in fatty foods, and the discoloration of foods high in carbohydrates, mentioned above. Cooks have long used salt, lemon, lime, or pineapple juice to control the discolora-

---

*The flavors that develop during reversion are quite different from rancid flavors. The word originated from the fact that certain fish oils "revert" to their original fishy smell when they are stored after processing. Soybean oil too is readily subject to reversion. In the process its odor changes from buttery to beany to grassy to painty and finally to fishy.

†Farm women learned long ago to store lard in a cool place and in containers with small openings so as to present the smallest surface area to the atmosphere. Darkness, coolness, and limited contact with air were the key elements in preventing rancidity.

tion of sliced peaches, apples, and potatoes. These citrus juices contain the natural antioxidant ascorbic acid,* also known as vitamin C, and the acid is widely used by food processors for this purpose.

The freezing of sliced peaches is a case in point. If antioxidants were not included, the peaches would become brown and unappetizing by the time they had thawed and were ready to eat. It is for this reason too that Breakstone, for example, uses ascorbic acid in its Swiss Parfait Peach Melba Yogurt. Wtihout it, the peaches would rapidly darken.

The chemicals most widely used by food processors to control both rancidity and browning are actually few in number. Butylated hydroxyanisole and its cousin butylated hydroxytolulene (usually listed as BHA and BHT so as not to alarm the consumer), are found in such products as General Foods' Tang, A & P's Smooth Whip, Kellogg's Pop Tarts, General Foods' Dream Whip, French's mashed potatoes, Ann Page's Sparkle, Louis Sherry's Shimmer, and many brands of crackers, soups, lard, and shortenings.

Because more than one antioxidant may be needed to produce the desired effect, propyl gallate is often used in combination with BHA or BHT. In addition, citric acid, phosphoric acid, and ascorbic acid are often added to enhance the effectiveness of BHA and BHT.

At times erythorbic acid or its sodium salt, sodium erythorbate, are used in chopped, ground, and cured meat products to prevent color fading. On the label of the smoked all-beef sausages called Slim Jims, it is noted: "Oxygen interceptor

---

*Ascorbic acid is a coined word, derived from *antiscorbutic*, which itself means effective against scurvy. The citrus fruits, especially lemons and limes, were used to prevent scurvy among sailors during long sea voyages.

added to improve stability." Because "antioxidant" might confuse or frighten some people, expressions such as this and "freshness stabilizer" (Pillsbury's Cinnamon Rolls with Icing; Betty Crocker's Sunkist Orange Frosting Mix; Duncan Hines cake mixes) are substituted.

When the B vitamins are added to enrich processed foods, as is often the case, you will rarely find them listed without an antioxidant such as BHA or BHT, for these vitamins are fatty in nature and quite susceptible to oxidation and rancidity.

Because of the naturally large quantity of oil in sunflower seeds, they must be well protected against rancidity. Accordingly, the label on Fisher's canned sunflower nuts lists not only BHA but also tricalcium phosphate and propyl gallate as antioxidants.

Once in a while you may notice another all but unpronounceable chemical, nordihydroguaiaretic acid, listed on a package of pie crust mix or an aerosol can of dessert topping. But this antioxidant, extracted from creosote, is losing ground to other more effective chemicals.

Housewives, unwrapping meats such as steak or ground beef, are often put off to notice a distinct difference in color between the surface and the interior of the meat. This in no way affects the quality of the meat, nor does it mean that the meat is rancid. The difference in color can be explained as follows: The principal pigment in meat tissue is myoglobin, a protein closely related to the hemoglobin of red blood cells. When meat is cut the myoglobin is exposed to the air, and forms oxymyoglobin, a particularly bright red pigment. The bluish or blue-purple color of the interior meat is the result of large amounts of myoglobin in combination with hemoglobin.

· **Sequestrants** ·

Chelating or sequestering agents are added to foods to bind up certain trace elements of metals such as copper, iron, and cobalt and render these metals chemically inactive. Chelating is a borrowing from the Greek *khele*, meaning claw, whereas sequestering comes from the Latin *sequestrare*, to give up for safekeeping.

The trace metals may be naturally present in certain foods, or they may find their way into them during processing. At all events these trace elements can lead to premature deterioration, off flavors, loss of colors, and clouding unless they are checked.

Many fats and oils, for example, contain traces of copper and iron. By themselves these metals do not produce rancidity, but they act as catalysts to hasten oxidative rancidity. Sequestrants combine with these metals and hold them in a tight complex so that they are no longer free to act as catalysts.

Among the natural chelates are chlorophyll, the green pigment of plants, and hemoglobin, the pigment of red blood cells. Both hold iron in a stable complex.

Sequestrants also play an important role in preventing clouding of what should be a clear soft drink. At times the water used by beverage bottlers contains minerals that tend to turn cloudy and settle on contact with the beverage's ingredients, particularly the coloring agents. The addition of a sequestrant will prevent this.

The pink discoloration seen in canned pears from time to time is another example of free trace metals reacting with chemicals in pear tissue. In this instance, a combination of copper, iron, and zinc are responsible.

A sequestrant gaining wide popularity in the food industry for its ability to prevent or significantly reduce discoloration, clouding, and rancidity is calcium disodium ethylene diamine tetraacetate, otherwise known as EDTA. For example, trace quantities of chromium, copper, and iron can produce a greenish-gray discoloration in canned whole-kernel and cream-style corn. By adding EDTA to the cans before heating, discoloration is prevented.

Often EDTA is used in conjunction with an antioxidant such as ascorbic acid, for the two work better together than either one alone. By adding a small amount of EDTA to cans of sliced peaches, for example, it is only necessary to add a quarter the amount of ascorbic acid that would otherwise have to be used.

High concentrations of iron, copper, and zinc are found in shellfish, particularly in shrimp. When heated and canned, shrimp can turn blue-green or grayish. Even uncooked iced shrimp undergo a black, spotty discoloration. As neither change is acceptable to the consumer, EDTA is added alone or in combination with citric acid to maintain the color of shrimp to the consumer's satisfaction.

Beer drinkers may be familiar with two problems that EDTA has gone a long way to solve. One is "chill haze," the other is "gushing." By sequestering the traces of iron usually contributed by the malt, gushing, or the sudden violent release of carbon dioxide when a beer bottle is opened, can be prevented. Chill haze appears to be the result of trace amounts of copper reacting with proteins in the malt. EDTA can prevent this, too, without adding any taste of its own to the beer.

TABLE 11
SEQUESTRANTS USED IN FOODS

Citric acid	Pepperidge Farm Frozen Apple Turnovers; Kellogg's Pop Tarts; Campbell's Cream of Potato Soup; My-T-Fine Lemon Flavor Pie Filling
Sodium citrate	General Foods Tang
Potassium citrate	Bird's Eye Awake
Disodium phosphate	Chelten House Instant Onion Chip Dip
Calcium disodium EDTA	Mayonette Low Calorie Imitation Mayonaise; Fannings Bread and Butter Pickles; Bonique Red Wine Vinegar and Oil Dressing
Tetrasodium pyrophosphate	Chelten House Instant Onion Chip Dip

The same EDTA used in foods as an additive is also used with great success to treat lead poisoning in children. It sequesters the lead, which is then excreted in the urine.

Table 11 lists half a dozen sequestering agents commonly used in processed foods.

· **Acidulants and Alkalies** ·

The fruit acids (named because they were originally derived from various fruits) are not only used to intensify the flavors in sherberts, for example, but to give the desired texture and tartness to process cheese and cheese spreads. Such is the case with Di-Et's Imitation Pasteurized Process Cheese Spread to which citric acid is added for tartness. The same chemical is added for the same reason to Nestea's lemon flavored ice tea mix. May-Bud Diet Snack Pizza Flavored Cheese Spread uses acetic acid to provide tartness, and Franco-American adds lactic acid in its beef gravy. Fumaric acid has a particularly low rate of moisture absorption, and so it is a valuable ingredient for extending the shelf life of many kinds of powdered food products. It is an ingredient in Jello's Wild Raspberry Gelatin Dessert, which also contains adipic acid that supplements the fruit flavor and imparts excellent setting qualities to all products containing gelatin.

Citric acid accounts for 60 percent of all acid additives. It is included in a broad spectrum of foods that include Mott's AM 5 Fruit Juice Drink, Campbell's Cream of Potato Soup, Pepperidge Farm's Frozen Apple Turnovers, Kellogg's Pop Tarts, and My-T-Fine's lemon flavored pie filling. Other acids such as phosphoric, fumaric, malic, adipic, tartaric, and lactic are found in many items, and each has its special characteristics. For example, an acid may be selected or rejected on the basis of its hygroscopicity (ability to absorb moisture), the ease with which it dissolves in water, its intensity of flavor, and its cost. Thus, although citric acid is the most readily soluble in water, fumaric acid is less expensive and more concentrated, so that less of it is needed to achieve the desired taste. Fumaric acid is also less hygroscopic than citric acid, and so it would be chosen for use in dry products where caking could be a problem.

Phosphoric acid is preferred for carbonated soft drinks and colas because it most effectively heightens the flavor of these drinks, and because of its sharp, quick-acting sourness.

The strong tartness of tartaric acid makes it ideal for augmenting fruit flavors. It is widely used in grape and lime flavored beverages, jams, jellies, and candies. A blend of tartaric and citric acids is often used in hard candies to achieve sour apple, wild cherry, and other especially tart flavors.

A name appearing on more and more products is adipic acid. It is less hygroscopic and has a blander flavor than citric acid and so can be used to good effect in such gelatin desserts as Jello's 1-2-3 Dessert Mix, and in Chelten House's Instant Onion Chip Dip, a dry mix. Like fumaric acid mentioned previously, adipic acid aids in setting mixtures containing gelatin, and in extending the shelf life of powdered products because of its low rate of moisture absorbtion.

TABLE 12

ORGANIC ACIDS OCCURRING NATURALLY
IN FRUITS AND VEGETABLES

Acid	Chemical Formula	Product
Malic	$C_4H_6O_5$	Apples, cherries, plums, cauliflower
Citric	$C_6H_8O_7$	Apricots, bananas, lemons, lima beans
Oxalic	$C_4H_8O_8$	Sorrel, rhubarb, apricots, blueberries
Tartaric	$C_4H_6O_6$	Grapes, apples, cherries
Benzoic	$C_6H_5CO_2HC_7H_6O_2$	Cranberries, benzoin, Peru and Tolu balsams
Succinic	$C_4H_6O_4$	Currants, cranberries
Quinic	$C_7H_{12}O_7$	Cranberries, carrot leaves, quinine, pears
Isocitric	$C_6H_8O_7$	Blueberries
Fumaric	$C_4H_4O_4$	Gooseberries, apples, watermelon

So as not to risk frightening the consumer with unfamiliar chemical names, many food manufacturers simply lump acid additives under the name "fruit acids." Table 12 lists some of these fruit acids.

At the opposite end of the scale are the alkalies that are used to prevent a food product from becoming too acid. Experience has shown that controlling the acidity can also improve flavor and lengthen shelf life.

Among the widely used alkalies are ammonium bicarbonate (found in Morton's frozen Coconut Cream Pie as well as in their frozen Chocolate Eclairs), sodium carbonate, and calcium carbonate. These compounds serve to reduce the acidity of wines and to control the acidity of canned peas and olives, among other products.

· Polyhydric Alcohols ·

Even the most phlegmatic consumer would have to have second thoughts on reading the words "polyhydric alcohols" on a label. It is simply not a term that inspires visions of home cooking. Fortunately this expression is never seen on food labels. However, the benign function of these chemicals belies their outrageous family name.

Organic chemists classify as polyhydric alcohols such substances as glycerine (glycerol), mannitol, sorbitol, and propylene glycol, which have one thing in common: they have more than one functional group in each molecule. In their case it is the hydroxyl or OH group.

Simple alcohols are classified as primary, secondary, or tertiary. A primary alcohol, such as ethyl alcohol, the major component of "booze," * is one in which the hydroxyl group is attached to a carbon atom holding only one other carbon.

Similarly, secondary and tertiary alcohols both have only one functional OH group. Polyhydric alcohols, or polyols, on the other hand, have (as the "poly" connotes) more than one functional OH group; in fact, they have at least three.

All four polyhydric alcohols have in common the ability

---

*It may be of interest to learn that "booze," or whiskey, got that nickname in the 1860's when a liquor dealer, E. G. Booz, made large numbers of whiskey bottles in the shape of log cabins. These became known as booze bottles and it wasn't long before whiskey became known as booze.

to readily absorb and retain water (in chemical terms they are hygroscopic), and thus are added to a number of foods to keep them moist.

There are many polyhydric alcohols, but only these four are permitted as direct food additives. All but propylene glycol can be found in nature. Although glycerine is naturally present in meats and vegetables combined in fatty acid molecules, it is obtained commercially as a major by-product of soap manufacture. Its formula is $C_3H_8O_3$ and its structure is

Sorbitol is present in pears, apples, and berries. Sorbitol, $C_6H_{14}O_6$, was originally isolated from the ripe berries of the mountain ash, *Sorbus aucuparia*. It has the following structure:

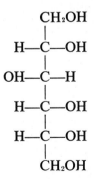

Whether obtained from natural products or made in a laboratory, these chemicals are added to processed foods to maintain their original condition during the weeks and months that may ensue between packaging and eating.

Depending upon its concentration and its relation to the

other ingredients, propylene glycol can act as a humectant, i.e., help to retain moisture. Its presence explains why marshmallows and shredded coconut no longer dry out as quickly as they used to. It is added to onion and garlic flavored croutons for the same reason.

Glycols can also act as softening agents; they can control sweetness, increase viscosity, or help another substance remain soluble. Chelten House's Instant Onion Chip Dip, for example, has propyl gallate in propylene glycol. The propyl gallate is an antioxidant, which requires the solvent action of the propylene glycol. Kellogg's Pop Tarts use the same two chemicals for the same reason.

One of the most interesting uses of sorbitol is to impart their unique consistency to certain kinds of candy, particularly to chocolate fondant fudge and peppermint patties. These confections stay relatively soft and chewy because their high sugar content is only partly crystallized owing to the high sorbitol content.

CHAPTER IV

How Safe Are They?

"Life is short, and art long; the occasion fleet-
ing; experience fallacious; and judgment difficult."

HIPPOCRATES

"We are carefully to preserve that life which
the Author of nature has given us, for it was
no idle gift."

HARVEY W. WILEY

In 1902 Harvey W. Wiley * established what popularly became known as "Dr. Wiley's Poison Squad" (see Figure 12).
By an Act of Congress this squad was set up "to enable the
Secretary of Agriculture to investigate the character of food
preservatives, coloring matters and other substances added

---

*Wiley was the first director of the Food and Drug Administration and
was largely responsible for moving Congress to enact the Pure Food and
Drug Act of 1906.

to foods, to determine their relation to digestion and health and to establish the principles which should guide their use."

Volunteers for the squad were recruited from among the employees of the Department of Agriculture. As Wiley later noted, "I wanted young, robust fellows with maximum resistance to deleterious effects of adulterated foods. . . . If they should show signs of injury after they were fed such substances for a period of time [none specified] the deduction would naturally follow that children and older persons more susceptible than they, would be greater sufferers from similar causes."

Twelve healthy men volunteered for the yearlong experiment. They pledged to eat and drink only what was given to them at meal times from the Department's kitchen, to continue to work at their ordinary jobs, and to take their usual amount of sleep.

Six of the volunteers were given a normal diet with the addition of the most common food preservative of the time —boric acid. The other six were given sodium borate (borax). When the experiment was over Wiley wrote in Bulletin 84 of the Department of Agriculture: "It appears . . . that both boric acid and borax (sodium borate) when continuously administered in small doses for a long period or when given in large quantites for a short period, creates disturbances of appetite, of digestion and of health." His conclusions were based on frequent physical examinations and a comparison of the foods given each man and his bodily excretions.

Unfortunately for Wiley, organ studies could not be performed, and the laboratory analyses of both urine and feces were extremely limited. Thus only relatively crude measurements could be made.

Prior to publication of these findings, an enterprising re-

Figure 12. Dr. Wiley, at the head of the table, and his poison squad sit down to a meal.

porter, seeking a story on the activities of the poison squad, wrote that Dr. Wiley had discovered that borax gave the volunteers a most beautiful pink complexion. The reporter did not mention that most of the men walked briskly to work even on frosty mornings. After the story broke, Dr. Wiley received innumerable letters from men and women all over the country, asking how borax should be taken in order to produce such a desirable cosmetic effect.

On this score little seems to have changed. Reporters still often prefer to write their own more colorful version of laboratory experiments, and people are still ready to believe and use anything that is mentioned in print no matter how flimsy the evidence.

During the nearly seven decades that have passed since Wiley's time, analytic procedures have attained a high degree of refinement, and our knowledge of the chemistry of tissues and cells has greatly increased. A number of physiologic reactions are still to be explained, but the testing of food additives today is sophisticated beyond anything that Harvey Wiley could have imagined.

Eating food and taking drugs or medicine are not the same. Bear in mind that drugs and medicine are used specifically for their ability to counter a disease process. For this purpose they are used at levels capable of producing a desired biologic effect and—this is particularly pertinent—with prior knowledge and acceptance that some toxic side effects may occur; additives share none of these characteristics.

By contrast, additives are placed into food at some point during processing. They may be lost or modified during a later stage of processing, or they may react with chemicals in the food to form a completely new substance. Thus, it is not enough to test a food additive *per se*. What is important is to test the additive in the form it reaches the consumer. And even then there are the variables of human appetite, age, sex, and state of health.

The question that has agonized a generation of toxicologists, biochemists, pharmacologists, and food scientists—and continues to do so—is how best to evaluate the safety of the chemicals we eat. The best answer today is to rely on the testing of an assortment of experimental animals and to extrapolate the results to human consumers.

The Pure Food and Drug Act of 1906 requires that our food supply be safe. The law states that substances (chemicals) may be added to food only under the following two conditions: that the substances be safe for human consumption and that they serve a useful purpose. An amendment to the Food, Drug and Cosmetic Act of 1938 provided the government with the leverage for enforcing the regulations, but it contained an inherent weakness. The Food and Drug Administration had to prove the presence of a deleterious substance before it could take action against it. For twenty-two years food processors and the FDA played "cops and robbers" while the public, as so often happens, was caught in the middle. The processors would slip in one additive or another and continue to sell the product until FDA researchers proved or disproved the safety of the chemical. The Color Additive Amendment of 1960 ended the farce by decreeing that no chemical can legally be used in any food until the *manufacturer* proves to the FDA that it is safe.

Consequently the FDA immediately had to decide what to do about all the additives then in use. They could either authorize the use of all of them under a "grandfather clause," or they could refuse to certify any of them until each one could be proved safe. In the resulting compromise, the FDA culled their lists and came up with 687 chemicals "generally *r*ecognized *a*s *s*afe" (GRAS) for their intended use. On the GRAS list are additives with a long history of safe use such as salt, pepper, vinegar, baking powder, monosodium glutamate, ascorbic acid, erythorbic acid, mustard, and so on.

The nonnutritive sweetener, cyclamate, was on the list until the recent decision to take it out of general use. Now saccharine, widely employed for 50 years, is being tested for safety while still remaining a GRAS item.

In his consumer message on October 30, 1969, President Nixon asked that the list of substances generally recognized as safe, and thus exempt from the safety certifications of the Food Additive Amendment of 1958, be fully reviewed and revised as necessary to assure adequate consumer safety.

As Dale R. Lindsay, Associate Commissioner for Science, FDA, noted, "some interpreted it as a mandate to immediately begin acute and chronic animal studies for each substance on the GRAS list." He went on to remark that given FDA's limited facilities "such a task was impossible, mandate or not." He added the point that "for a good many of these substances, and for the uses made of them, no cogent reasons existed for doubting their safety; no justification could be made for the funds required to test them."

Apparently present intentions are not to eliminate the GRAS list but to establish a set of priorities for testing selected items. Saccharine and monosodium glutamate have received top priority. Because it would take hundreds of years of animal testing to establish methodically the efficacy and safety for human consumption of everything on the GRAS list, the list is being evaluated by toxicologists and pharmacologists, who are recommending laboratory tests where appropriate.

It is fair to say that most intentional food additives (not to be confused with adulterants) are not inherently harmful. Because of the extremely low levels of additives used in foods, enormous quantities would have to be ingested at one time to produce adverse effects. The "sword" that hangs over the head of most food scientists, however, is the uncertainty about the consequences of ingetsing the low levels of additives over a protracted period. Because direct observation of consumers is not feasible, tests are usually carried out on an assortment of animals: mice, rats, rabbits, guinea pigs, dogs, cats, and monkeys. Both long- and short-term feeding studies are usually carried out (long term generally being for the lifespan of the animal) and the levels of additives in the test animals' diet are far higher than the levels contemplated for human food. In extrapolating the results to man, the general rule is that the additive is safe if it produces no adverse physiologic effects in the test animals at a level at least 100 times higher than that to be used in human food.

The movement toward systematic testing of additive began in 1943 with the publication of an FDA report.* The researchers noted that "increased exposure to toxic substances is a consequence of modern civilization," and they proposed that "in order better to understand the problems of acute and chronic toxicity resulting from such exposures, well controlled toxicological investigations must be carried out," and that "the levels causing *acute, subacute,* and *chronic* toxicity be accurately determined in several species of animals." Their report included a protocol for testing that with some modifications and extensions remains the basis for current research. Tables 13 and 14 present up-to-date versions of the essential features contained in their protocol.

Some 25 years later, the World Health Organization convened an international panel of experts to consider a similar problem on a world basis. In their report, "Procedures for Investigating Intentional and Unintentional Food Additives," they made the point that "three particular aspects of toxicology require consideration in this connection: first, the choice of the most appropriate animal species for investigations that aim at the prediction of human responses; secondly, the investigation of a reversible specific effect observed in the most

---

*"Acute and Chronic Toxicity: Public Health Aspects," by Geoffrey Woodard and Herbert O. Calvery, *Industrial Medicine,* **12,** 55–59, 1943.

TABLE 13
GENERAL PROTOCOL OF TOXICOLOGIC TESTS TO BE PERFORMED

I.   Acute tests (single dose)
 A. LD_{50} determination (24 hour test and survivors followed for 7 days)
   1. Two species (one that is not a rodent)
   2. Two routes of administration (one by intended route of use if other than by topical contact)
II. Prolonged tests (daily doses)
 A. Duration—3 months
 B. Two species (usually rats and dogs)
 C. Three dose levels
 D. Route of administration according to intended route of use
 E. Evaluation of state of health
   1. All animals weighed weekly
   2. Complete physical examination weekly
   3. Blood chemistry,* urinalysis, hematologic exam,† and function tests performed on all ill animals
 F. Those animals given the high doses as well as the control animals subjected to complete autopsy including histologic examination of all organ systems
III. Chronic tests (daily doses)
 A. Duration—1 to 2 years
 B. Species—selected from results of prior prolonged tests, pharmacodynamic studies on several species of animals, possibly single dose human trial studies. Otherwise use two species, one of which is not a rodent.
 C. Three dose levels
 D. Route of administration according to intended route of use
 E. Evaluation of state of health
   1. All animals weighed weekly
   2. Complete physical examination weekly
   3. Blood chemistry, urinalysis, hematologic examination, and function tests on all animals at 6-month intervals and on all ill or abnormal animals

---

*Blood chemistry includes: sodium, potassium, blood urea nitrogen, glucose.
†Hematologic examination includes: hematocrit, total red blood cell counts, total and differential white blood cell counts. thrombocyte counts.

    F.   Those animals given the high doses as well as the control animals subjected to complete autopsy including histologic examination of all organ systems

IV.   Special tests

    A.   For potentiation with other chemicals

    B.   For effects on fertility

    C.   For teratogenicity

    D.   For carcinogenicity

Urinalysis:

       pH and specific gravity

       protein

       glucose

       ketones

       crystals

       blood cells

       bacteria

Organ Function Tests:

       Bromsulphalein retention (liver function)

       Serum alkaline phosphatase (liver function)

       SGOT—Serum glutamoxaltransaminase (heart function)

---

sensitive animal species to determine whether it represents a significant hazard to man; thirdly, the study of effects specific to man."

To this end, three fundamental tests are performed on laboratory animals for the purpose of detecting the toxic effects of a given chemical in man. These tests differ primarily in their duration. *Acute* tests require only a single large dose of the additive. *Prolonged* or *subchronic* tests last at least three months, during which time the additive is included in the diet at least once daily. *Chronic toxicity, long-term,* or *extended* studies are those in which the animals are fed the additive daily for one to two years, or for the length of the animal's life.

TABLE 14
SIGNS* AND SYMPTOMS† FOUND ON ANIMALS UNDERGOING
TOXICOLOGIC TESTS

Signs

Aggressiveness toward experimenter
Altered muscle tone
Alterations in cardiac rate and rhythm
Catatonia (phases of stupor or excitement)
Coma
Convulsions to touch
Paralysis
Change in pupillary size
Sensitivity to pain
Skin lesions
Corneal opacities
Placing reflexes
Righting reflexes
Grasping reflexes
Death

Symptoms

Abnormal excreta
Exploratory behavior
Inactivity
Convulsions, spontaneous
Dyspnea (shortness of breath)
Sedation (calming)
Nystagmus (involuntary rapid movements of eyeballs)
Cyanosis
Salivation
Nasal discharge
Piloerection (erection of hair)
Phonation (utterance of vocal sounds)
Unusual physical positions
Unusual tail positions

*Signs—those things usually found on physical or clinical examination.
†Symptoms—those things readily seen on observation.

As noted earlier, food additives are not drugs, and they are not usually tested in the same way. Whereas a drug may be tested by injection or any number of other routes (see Table 15), the additive must be taken orally. From the mouth, where digestion begins, it passes into the stomach and on into the small intestine. From the small intestine (duodenum, jejunum, ileum) absorption and distribution throughout the body occurs via the bloodstream.

What disturbs scientists is the interpretation of test results obtained when additives are injected directly into the abdomen, or when pellets of additive are surgically implanted into the bladder or other organs. Too often such experiments produce extraordinary results that cannot reasonably be extrapolated to man.

TABLE 15
PARENTERAL* ROUTES OF ADMINISTRATION

Route	Clinical Expression
Beneath skin	subcutaneous
Into skin	intradermal
Into muscle	intramuscular
Into vein	intravenous
Into spinal fluid	intrathecal
Into artery	intraarterial
Into chest fluid	intrapleural
Into abdominal area	intraperitoneal
Into cells	intracellular

*Requiring inoculation with syringe and hollow needle.

· **Acute Toxicity Testing** ·

The purpose of acute testing is to determine quickly the effects of feeding high levels of an additive at one time. From zero to at least four concentrations of the additive level producing significant results are fed to groups of animals. Control groups are not usually used, nor are autopsies performed to determine the type and extent of physiologic effects. However, keen observation of the animals' symptoms will allow the investigator to arrive at a number of conclusions about where and how the substance produced its effect. (See again Table 14 [signs and symptoms].) The acute tests also provide the researcher with a particularly instructive value— the LD_{50}. This is the toxilocoligst's shorthand for the *l*ethal *d*ose that kills 50 percent of the population being studied.

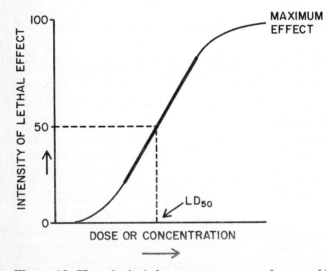

Figure 13. Hypothetical dose-response curve for an additive fed to a population of animals

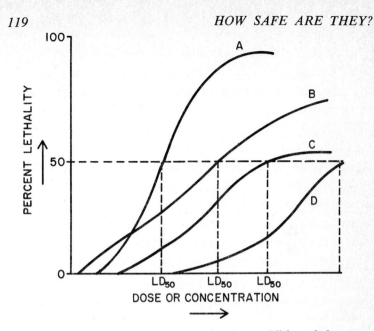

Figure 14. Dose-response curves for four additives fed to a population of animals

It is obtained by plotting a dose-response graph such as that in Figure 13.

As a result of picking a concentration of additive that will kill 50 percent of whatever animal population is under study, an S-shaped or sigmoidal curve is obtained. Establishing the LD_{50} allows the researcher to compare the toxicity * of one chemical with that of another by comparing the slopes or degree of steepness of the curves. The steeper the rise the more potent the chemical, as you can see from Figure 14, which plots the results of feeding four hypothetical additives.

---

*This term has been used several times and perhaps needs definition. Toxicity is the capacity of a substance to produce injury, whereas hazard, another widely used term, is the probability that injury will result from use of a chemical if the substance is used in the manner and quantity proposed.

The curve for D indicates that it is the least potent of the four. Clearly, the slope of the dose-response curve may be the most important value obtained when comparing a series of substances.

Advances in science result from the cumulative work of many men, but I believe it is fair to say that in 1927, J. W. Trevan of the Wellcome Physiological Research Laboratories (England) developed the concept of LD_{50}. Working with exceptionally large numbers of frogs, he showed that unless many animals are used in an acute test, only inaccurate results are obtained. Only large numbers will average out the wide variability of response among individuals in a species. Accordingly, acute studies today are usually conducted on 30 to 40 animals at each of at least four dosage levels.

Although the LD_{50} data are of little value in assessing the actual safety of a potential additive, they do act as guides for determining concentration levels to be employed in prolonged and chronic tests, and they give some indication of the biologic effects that the additive may have on the test animals.

· **Prolonged or Subacute Studies** ·

The single dose of a food additive that is administered in acute tests is hardly typical of human experience. Few, if any, foods are eaten only once. Accordingly, prolonged tests are set up to follow closely the conditions under which the additive would be used for human consumption. These tests, which last a minimum of three months,* are made on two

*In 1959, the Food Protection Committee of the NAS–NRC stated that "it is seldom worthwhile to carry them out for a period of less than 90 days. . . ."

different species of animals, usually rats and dogs. This is because of the wide spectrum of responses to any chemical that is commonly seen within and among animal species.

The prolonged tests are run on at least four groups of animals. Each group is made up of a minimum of ten male and ten female animals of the same species. One group, the control, is fed no additive at all. The second is usually given ten times more than the amount suggested for use in human food; the third gets a dose halfway between the second and the fourth group's. The fourth group is given the highest amount the animals can tolerate, as determined by the LD_{50} of the acute study.

Test animals must all be healthy speciments, and they must be maintained in an environment wherein temperature, humidity, light, and cleanliness are rigidly controlled. In addition, all animals must be carefully observed for at least two weeks before tests begin so that the researcher may note their normal behavior in their normal physical state.

Once the test has begun, the animals must be observed and weighed weekly. Cages must be inspected for evidence that food and water are being adequately consumed, and that excreta is or is not normal. Exact records must be kept of of the symptoms of all groups including the control group. Animals that die during the course of the study must undergo a necropsy which includes microscopic examination of tissues from the liver, spleen, kidney, pancreas, adrenal glands, heart, brain, bone marrow, gonads, and other organs. If any other tissues appear abnormal on inspection, they, too, will be examined under the microscope.

The data collected during the study often include the amounts of food consumed, growth rate, weight, blood and urine analyses, and behavioral patterns.

At the end of the study all surviving animals are sacrificed and a complete autopsy of all tissues is performed. From the data obtained, it can be decided whether the additive is too hazardous to warrant further study, or whether it appears to be safe but requires additional testing.

It will be immediately evident that a prolonged test is extremely expensive, considering the number and quality of animals involved and the degree of detailed observation necessary.

· Chronic, Long-Term, or Extended Tests ·

Chronic tests differ from prolonged tests only in magnitude and duration. Chronic tests usually last for the lifetime of an animal. They are based on the assumption that "The effects of the lifetime ingestion of an additive in food by man cannot be predicted from results of experiments less stringent than lifetime feeding in a short-lived mammal (18 to 24 months in the case of the rat) and one year or longer feeding in the dog or monkey . . . these studies may be either inadequate or more exacting than necessary *but experience has not supplied a more rational alternative*." * [Italics author's.]

In their highly respected publication, "Experimental Methods Used in Determining Chronic Toxicity: A Critical Review," † J. M. Barnes and F. A. Denz stated that little useful data could be obtained from animal feeding studies that lasted longer than six months. They asked: "What information can

---

*From "Principles and Procedures for Evaluating the Safety of Food Additives," 750, December 1959; prepared by the Food Protection Committee of the National Academy of Sciences, National Research Council.
†*Pharmacological Review*, **6**: 191–242, 1954.

be culled from the sterile survivors of a two year experiment?" Noting that the normal rate of attrition removes 70 to 90 percent of any given sample of rats at the end of two years, they calculated that if the usual 10 to 20 animals are used per test, only 2 to 3 would remain to be evaluated at the end of that time—hardly a significant statistical sampling from which to draw conclusions. "Much that is confusing and conflicting in chronic toxicity tests," they go on to say, "arises from these studies on rodent geriatrics and many of the conclusions based on the pathological studies of the survivors reflect in turn the skill, experience and prejudice of the pathologist."

So as not to end a chronic test with so few animals, present protocols call for using at least 30 to 40 rats of each sex and at least 30 to 40 at each feeding level. Here again, a control group must be included to disclose the normal effect of aging and avoid confusing them with the effects produced by the test chemical. Of course the levels of additive used must not kill all the animals. If this happens, the results will be meaningless and the test will have to be repeated.

The species of animal used in the tests is yet another cause for concern. Although they must be healthy, the fact is that there is little point and even less to be gained by spending a year, two, or more in feeding animals whose systems are grossly different from our own in ability to absorb, metabolize, or excrete the additive. Accordingly, researchers believe it worthwhile to spend time ascertaining the most suitable animal types to be used.

Feeding is begun shortly after weaning and is continued for at least 1½ years. During this period the full range of observations and the physical biochemical tests noted for the prolonged studies are performed. Additional tests are also carried out to determine possible carcinogenic, reproductive, and mutagenic effects of the chemical under study. Because these types of effects are slow to manifest themselves, they are not possible to observe in the prolonged studies.

On completion of chronic studies, the data must be extrapolated to man. This presents a number of difficulties. For example, after more than a year of reviewing the various methods of evaluating the safety of food additives and pesticide residues, an advisory panel convened by the FDA reported * that a three-generation reproduction study was needed to evaluate those hazards. The panel cited an earlier report † on the harmful effects of low levels of pesticides. That report stated that these harmful effects became visible only after a number of successive generations of test animals had been depleted of their stored nutrients.

Three-generation studies, which are not usually made as part of the chronic toxicity tests, are most useful for detecting whether additives as well as pesticides are hazardous to the normal development of a fertilized ovum or whether they lower fertility (gametogenesis) and whether they contribute to genetic damage (mutagenesis) or congenital malformations such as the seal limb condition (phocomelia) that afflicted gestating embryos of mothers who had used the sedative Thalidomide during the first trimester of pregnancy.

Thalidomide is a drug and not a food additive, but its tragic effects alerted investigators to the vulnerability of fetuses in the uterus to substances that in no way harm the pregnant mother. Whereas it was well known that a virus such

---

*"Food and Drug Administration Advisory Committee on Protocols for Safety Evaluations: Panel on Reproduction Report on Reproduction Studies in the Safety Evaluation of Food Additives and Pesticide Residues" published in *Toxicology and Applied Pharmacology*, **16**:264–96, 1970.

†By Dr. O. Garth Fitzhugh of the Division of Toxicological Evaluation of the FDA.

as that producing rubella (German measles) could seriously affect the growing fetus,* no thought had been given to the possibility that chemicals or drugs could do so too.

According to the FDA panel's report, testing additives for their capacity to cause reproductive injury over three generations "provides the opportunity for accumulation of substances or insult to the point where deleterious effects may be observed." Soon after weaning, the test animals are placed on their respective diets. Matings are allowed to occur (in the case of rats, when they are 100 days old). On the birth of each litter, records are made as to the number born live or stillborn. The weight of each pup is recorded along with its physical condition and any observable abnormality.

On weaning, the first generation animals are reexamined and then sacrificed, and an autopsy is made to see if they have any internal abnormalities.

The parents (F_0 in Table 16) are then remated and the next generation is examined as was the first. However, only some of the litter are now selected for sacrifice; the majority are allowed to continue on the test diet and then mated. This procedure is repeated through three generations. Table 16 sets forth this concept graphically.

A chronic toxicity study may yield significant information about the potential or actual cancer-causing (carcinogenic) properties of the chemical under study. If one problem can be said to pose the greatest difficulty, this is it. The toxicologist's major worry is that a substance found to be relatively nontoxic in animals will prove to be carcinogenic to man. Here it may be of help to point out that there appears to

---

*German measles has been known to produce cataracts, deafness, microcephely, cardiac malformations, clubfoot, and cleft palate.

TABLE 16

PLAN FOR A THREE-GENERATION REPRODUCTION STUDY

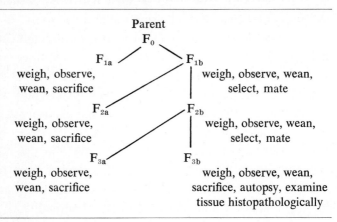

Parent
F_0

F_{1a}

weigh, observe,
wean, sacrifice

F_{1b}

weigh, observe, wean,
select, mate

F_{2a}

weigh, observe,
wean, sacrifice

F_{2b}

weigh, observe, wean,
select, mate

F_{3a}

weigh, observe,
wean, sacrifice

F_{3b}

weigh, observe, wean,
sacrifice, autopsy, examine
tissue histopathologically

be no relationship between systemic toxicity (the capacity to produce injury) and the capacity to cause cancer. In fact, it is almost a rule that the toxic dose of a carcinogen is higher than the carcinogenic dose.

Often chronic tests are carried on for four and five years (particularly with dogs, monkeys, and the longer-lived mammals) in order to avoid false or misleading results. This is because all animals exhibit the phenomenon of naturally occurring spontaneous tumor formation. In addition, one species of animal may be resistant to agents known to be carcinogenic in other species. Thus tests for carcinogenicity require large numbers as well as several species of animals, if the results are to be meaningful.

With the completion of animal testing there remains the task of transferring the data to man. Acute, subacute, and chronic tests have shown the additive to be safe in animals. Does this mean it will be safe for human use? Conversely, if an additive is found to be carcinogenic in animals, does it mean it will do the same in humans? Unfortunately we can never learn this because the Delaney Amendment of 1958 proscribes the use of such an additive for man once it is found hazardous to animals.

The cyclamates are an excellent case in point. Given evidence, however controversial, of its toxicity in rats, the FDA was obliged under the Delaney Amendment to prohibit their use for humans. As Robert Finch, then secretary of the Department of Health, Education, and Welfare said, "The Delaney Amendment should be modified to permit some scientific rationality in making these decisions. If we were to apply the criteria of the Delaney Amendment across the board, eventually we would be reduced to a nation of vegetarians and even some of the vegetables would have to be banned."

There are obviously differences between men and animals. The main question is: Are the differences so great that data gleaned from animal studies have little value when extrapolated to man? Few, if any, scientists would argue that animal tests are without value; most would point to their limitations, but would accept data from rigorous studies.

No animal has yet been found that metabolizes additives or drugs exactly as man does. Some breeds of dogs metabolize certain chemicals in a manner resembling man. The chimpanzee's metabolism is even closer to man's, but again only for a few specific chemicals.

The following two recent findings illustrate the complexity of extrapolating data from animal studies to man.

Cycasin, a glucoside * obtained from the seeds of a fern-like cousin to the gingko tree, is nontoxic to rats when injected. However, when given orally it is both toxic to the liver and carcinogenic because it is split (hydrolized) by the

---

*A glucoside is one of the many glycosides, which are compounds containing a carbohydrate as part of their molecular structures. In this case the carbohydrate is glucose.

rats' intestinal bacteria to a toxic aglycone (the noncarbo-
hydrate of the glucoside). Similarly, rats fed on a diet containing cyclamates have been found to excrete large quantities
of cyclohexylamine, which is the product that has been considered potentially harmful to humans. In both cases the
conversion of one substance into another is accomplished by
the rat's gut bacteria.

The trouble is that man has few bacteria in the jejunum
and proximal ileum (parts of the small intestine), whereas
rodents have abundant bacteria throughout the gut. In addition, most of man's gut flora belong to a different genus than
the rodent's flora.* Finally, in the human digestive process,
most food is absorbed into the body proper before it reaches
the region of the intestines where exposure to bacterial enzymes (metabolism and splitting) occurs. Therefore, the
potential toxicity of a chemical to human beings cannot legiti-
mately be determined by testing only rodents.

Even if several species of animals are selected for testing
a given chemical, their respective metabolic patterns must be
known in advance. Thus, for example, quinic acid (found in
tea, apples, and other fruit, tobacco leaves, and chinchona
bark) is modified by the gut bacteria of Old World monkeys,
but not modified by the gut bacteria of New World monkeys.†
or dogs, cats, rats, and guinea pigs. Unfortunately, this

---

*Man's belong primarily to the genus *Escherichria*; rodents' to the genera
Bacterioides and *Bifidobacterium*.
†Old World monkeys are so called because they are found in Africa and
Asia. Examples are the rhesus (Macaca), baboon (Papio), and green
(Cercopithecus).
  New World monkeys, the squirrel (Saimiri), spider (Ateles), and capuchin
(Cebres), are found in Central and South America. All monkeys belong
to one of these two groups. It is believed that, some 30 million years ago
when the continents had not yet separated, both groups had a common
ancestor.

kind of information is extremely difficult to obtain and is only beginning to be màde available.

To further confound the difficulty of evaluating the effects of chemicals on man, pharmacologists from Sweden's Karolinska Institute, in collaboration with a team from the U.S. National Heart and Lung Institute, have found that drugs vary widely in their effect on individual human beings. Given equal doses of a drug, its level in the blood was found to vary as much as thirty to fifty times from person to person.

The researchers presented their findings at a New York Academy of Sciences conference on drug metabolism in man. At the same meeting another report stated: "It appears that the interaction between drugs may be critical in producing toxic—or no—reactions." In other words one drug may cancel or intensify the effect of another. The difficulty remains when these findings are translated from drugs to food additives.

Such discrepancies on metabolism between different species of animals and even between one man and another show how important it is to employ more than one species of animal when testing a potential additive. Recently, brominated vegetable oils were found hazardous on the basis of rat studies alone. As a result, the FDA ordered beverage producers either to eliminate this stabilizer or to bring it within "safe" tolerance levels. Small amounts of brominated oils are used to adjust the density of essential oils used in soft drinks, and these oils produce a clouding effect. When scientists of the Food and Drug Directorate of Canada found that rats given high doses of the oils developed degenerative heart lesions, the United States FDA took the cue and passed its order along to American beverage producers. The Canadian FDD, on the other hand, did not consider the oils a threat to health, provided that no more than 5 milligrams were added per 10-ounce bottle.

Another example of the difficulty in extrapolating animal data to man concerns BHT, butylated hydroxytoluene, a widely used antioxidant. In 1959, four Australian investigators reported that BHT fed to rats in "relatively large doses" was not safe for use in human food. Within a short time, unfounded newspaper reports told of rats born bald and eyeless. In 1965, after a thorough review of the data on BHT from both human and animal studies, a joint committee of experts convened by the World Health Organization and the Food and Agriculture Organization of the United Nations approved the use of BHT as an additive to human foods at specific tolerance levels.

Unfortunately for both consumers and producers alike, the early distorted press accounts of the effects of BHT on rats will be hard dying. Paradoxically, far from being harmful, BHT may possibly add years to our lives. A University of Nebraska physician has reported in the *Journal of Gerontology* * that a diet containing 0.5 percent BHT produced a 45 percent increase in life span in a test group of mice. The hypothesis tested was that free radicals,† highly reactive molecular fragments, play a role in aging by causing the deterioration of cells, and that BHT, both an antioxidant and a free-radical inhibitor, can stop or interfere with free-radical reactions.

Dr. Harman noted that if such changes do play a role in

---

*"Free Radical Theory of Aging: Effects of Free Radical Reaction Inhibitors on the Mortality Rate of Male LAF Mice," by Dr. Denham Harman. *Journal of Gerontology*, **23**:476, 1968.

†Methane or marsh gas, CH_4, is the simplest of all organic compounds, having only one carbon atom. With its four hydrogen atoms, it is a particularly stable substance. Losing one of its hydrogens, it becomes the free radical methyl which is now highly reactive. In this condition, it can readily combine with another methyl radical to form another stable compound, ethane.

aging, the aging process may be slowed by the addition of nontoxic antioxidants to food. In so doing, the concentration of compounds in the body capable of reacting rapidly with free radicals would be significantly raised, thereby affording fewer of them the opportunity for harmful reactions. Perhaps the injunction, eat to live, is correct after all.

Another example of the unnecessary hysteria that can be generated by premature press reports concerns monosodium glutamate. Dr. John W. Olney, a Washington University psychiatrist, injected large doses of MSG into newborn and adult mice. In short order, the infant mice incurred brain damage, while the adults showed stunted skeletal development, marked obesity, and sterility in the females. As a result of almost immediate public outcry and congressional hearings, the National Research Council convened its Food and Nutrition Board to evaluate the safety of MSG. After a careful appraisal the board found MSG suitable for consumption by adults and noted that "it considers it unnecessary to recommend any restriction at the present time in foods for other than infants." Its report went on to say that the board's evaluation of published studies "revealed no risk in the use of MSG as a food component," and that there was "no intended implication" in its findings that MSG "is not suitable or safe for use in infant foods" since it did not consider the question. Nevertheless, shortly thereafter the major baby food manufacturers announced that MSG would be eliminated from their recipes pending further study of its safety.

MSG is extensively used in Chinese cooking and has often been incriminated in the "Chinese Restaurant Syndrome" (CRS).* Recently two Italian scientists, P. L. Morselli and

---

*CRS is often reported as a burning sensation in the back of the neck, spreading to the forearms and to the anterior thorax, accompanied by a feeling of infraorbital pressure, tightness, and substernal discomfort.

S. Garatini of the Institute of Pharmacologic Research, Milan, reported* that the CRS may simply be a case of autosuggestion. They fed beef broth with and without MSG to seven female and seventeen male volunteers aged eighteen to thirty-four. Those who had received broth without MSG claimed to be suffering from a number of CRS symptoms, whereas those who ate the broth containing MSG had no such symptoms.

Because of the many complexities of safety testing an additive and extrapolating the results to man, and because the present state of toxicologic knowledge does not allow for anything approaching certainty, some margin of safety is necessary in making up specifications for the human consumption of additives. That margin of safety has varied from 10 to 500 times less than the maximum amount of additive shown to be harmless in animal tests. The margin most often used is 100 times because of the wide range of potential human consumers—some infants, some aged, some sick, and some healthy.

Consumers' and food processors' lives would be far less complicated if there were a simple answer to the question: "Is it poisonous?" Unfortunately, there isn't. As Dr. P. S. Elas, Senior Medical Officer (Toxicology) of the British Ministry of Health has aptly said †: "In principle no chemicals are ever harmless, there are only harmless ways of using them and the greatest necessity is the balancing of benefits against risks."

Common table salt, for example, is essential to life, yet a

---

*Nature, 227, August 8, 1970.
†Speaking at a Congress on the Sanitary Protection of Food held in Milan, Italy, in April, 1970.

large amount absorbed in a short time would probably kill the eater. Many metals such as copper, manganese, zinc, and cobalt are essential to health in trace amounts, but become poisonous in larger quantities. Overdoses of both vitamins A and D can cause severe damage to the human system.

Several years ago a Philadelphia fish dealer dosed 1800 pounds of spoiled flounder fillets with sodium nitrate to mask their off odor and color. Sodium nitrate, or chili saltpeter, is one of the most abundant naturally occurring nitrates, and when used judiciously is rather innocuous. Since the Middle Ages, for example, it has been used to maintain the red color of meat. But nitrates in sufficient quantities can cause a rapid drop in blood pressure by enlarging the blood vessels of the consumer.

In this instance, the Philadelphia dealer's flounder fillets were shipped to Pennsylvania and New Jersey markets. Within a short time 150 people became ill with nitrate "poisoning." Many were hospitalized and a three-year-old child in Haddon Heights, New Jersey, died. Others, of course, survived the same fish without discomfort. Thus any definition of a poison must take into account the dose administered as well as the age, sex, and mental and physical health of the consumer.

At this point it may be as well to raise the question, how does the producer or marketer of a food additive satisfy the Food and Drug Administration that his product is safe?

To accomplish this, the federal government, through the FDA, has established a petitioning procedure designed to protect both consumer and producer that allows both sides "its day in court." Most often the proceedings leading to approval or disapproval take months, or even years.

The petition initiated by a manufacturer must specify the

FEDERAL REGISTER

VOLUME 35 · **NUMBER 95**

Friday, May 15, 1970 · Washington, D.C.

Pages 7545–7630

Agencies in this issue—

Detailed list of Contents appears inside.

Title 21—FOOD AND DRUGS

Chapter I—Food and Drug Administration, Department of Health,
Education, and Welfare

SUBCHAPTER B—FOOD AND FOOD PRODUCTS

PART 121—FOOD ADDITIVES

Subpart A—Definitions and Proce-
dural and Interpretative Regulations

GLYCINE IN FOOD FOR HUMAN
CONSUMPTION

Pursuant to provisions of the Federal
Food, Drug, and Cosmetic Act (secs. 201
(s), 409, 701(a), 52 Stat. 1055, 72 Stat.
1784–88, as amended; 21 U.S.C. 321(s),
348, 371(a)) and under authority dele-
gated to the Commissioner of Food and
Drugs (21 CFR 2.120), the following new
statement of policy is added to Part 121,
Subpart A:

§ 121.12 Glycine in food for human
consumption; statement of policy.

(a) Heretofore, the Food and Drug
Administration has expressed the opinion
in trade correspondence that glycine
is generally recognized as safe for certain
technical effects in human food when
used in accordance with good manufacturing practice; however:

(1) Reports in scientific literature indicate that adverse effects were found in
cases where high levels of glycine were
administered in diets of experimental
animals.

(2) Current usage information indicates that the daily dietary intake of
glycine by humans may be substantially
increasing due to changing use patterns
in food technology.

Therefore, the Food and Drug Administration no longer regards glycine and
its salts as generally recognized as safe
for use in human food and all outstanding letters expressing sanction for such
use are rescinded.

(b) The Commissioner of Food and
Drugs concludes that in the public interest and within 180 days after publication of this section in the FEDERAL
REGISTER, manufacturers:

(1) Shall reformulate food products
for human use to eliminate added glycine and its salts; and

(2) Shall bring such products into
compliance with an authorizing food
additive regulation. A food additive petition supported by toxicity data is required to show that any proposed level of
glycine or its salts added to food for
human consumption will be safe.

(c) The status of glycine as generally
recognized as safe for use in animal feed,
as prescribed in § 121.101(d)(5), remains
unchanged because the additive is considered an essential nutrient in certain
animal feeds and is safe for such use
under conditions of good feeding
practice.

(Secs. 201(s), 409, 701(a), 52 Stat. 1055, 72
Stat. 1784–88, as amended; 21 U.S.C. 321(s),
348, 371(a))

Figure 15. The cover of the Federal Register and a typical regulation published in it

CALCIUM CYCLAMATE

Calcium Cyclohexanesulfamate

$$\left[\langle \bigcirc \rangle -NH-SO_2-OCaO-SO_2-NH-\langle \bigcirc \rangle \right] 2H_2O$$

$C_{12}H_{24}CaN_2O_6S_2 . 2H_2O$ Mol. wt. 432.58

DESCRIPTION

White odorless crystals or crystalline powder. In dilute solutions it is about 30 times as sweet as sucrose. Its solutions are neutral to litmus. One gram is soluble in about 4 ml. of water, in about 1.5 ml. of propylene glycol, and in about 60 ml. of alcohol. It is practically insoluble in chloroform and in ether.

IDENTIFICATION

A. To 10 ml. of a 1 in 100 solution add 1 ml. of hydrochloric acid, mix, and add 1 ml. of barium chloride T.S. The solution remains clear, but upon the addition of 1 ml. of sodium nitrite solution (1 in 10), a white precipitate is formed.

B. A 1 in 100 solution gives positive tests for *Calcium*, page 769.

SPECIFICATIONS

Assay. Not less than 98 per cent and not more than the equivalent of 101 per cent of $C_{12}H_{24}CaN_2O_6S_2$, calculated on the anhydrous basis.

Water. Between 6 per cent and 9 per cent.

Limits of Impurities

Arsenic (as As). Not more than 3 parts per million (0.0003 per cent).

Heavy metals (as Pb). Not more than 10 parts per million (0.001 per cent).

Selenium. Not more than 30 parts per million (0.003 per cent).

TESTS

Assay. Dissolve about 400 mg., previously dried at 105° for 1 hour and accurately weighed, in a mixture of 50 ml. of water and 5 ml. of hydrochloric acid, and titrate with 0.1 *M* sodium nitrite. Add the last ml. of titrant dropwise until a blue color is produced immediately when a glass rod dipped into the titrated solution is streaked on a piece of starch iodide test paper. When the titration is complete, the end-point is reproducible after the mixture has been allowed to stand for 1 minute. Each ml. of 0.1 *M* sodium nitrite is equivalent to 19.83 mg. of $C_{12}H_{24}Ca$-$N_2O_6S_2$.

Water. Determine by the *Karl Fischer Titrimetric Method*, page 804.

Arsenic. A *Sample Solution* prepared as directed for organic compounds meets the requirements of the *Arsenic Test*, page 720.

Heavy metals. Prepare and test a 2-gram sample as directed in *Method II* under the *Heavy Metals Test*, page 763, using 20 mcg. of lead ion (Pb) in the control (*Solution A*).

Selenium. Prepare and test a 2-gram sample as directed in the *Selenium Limit Test*, page 787.

Packaging and storage. Store in well-closed containers.

Functional use in foods. Non-nutritive sweetener.

Figure 16. Standard for a food-grade chemical as published in the Food Chemicals Codex

ADDITIONS, CHANGES, AND CORRECTIONS

Changes and additions listed herein constitute revisions in the Food Chemicals Codex, First Edition, effective December 1, 1969. Page numbers cited refer to F.C.C. I, unless otherwise specified.

Aluminum Sulfate, page 32

Change the SPECIFICATION for *Assay* to read:

Assay. $Al_2(SO_4)_3$ (anhydrous), not less than 99.5 per cent of $Al_2(SO_4)_3$; $Al_2(SO_4)_3 . 18H_2O$ (hydrate), not less than 99.5 per cent and not more than the equivalent of 114 per cent of $Al_2(SO_4)_3 . 18H_2O$. [*Note*—The upper limit of 114 per cent of $Al_2(SO_4)_3 . 18H_2O$ corresponds to approximately 101.7 per cent of $Al_2(SO_4)_3 . 14H_2O$.]

Change the paragraph entitled *Heavy metals*, page 33, to read:

Heavy metals. Dissolve 500 mg. in 20 ml. of water, add a few drops of diluted hydrochloric acid T.S., and evaporate to dryness in a porcelain dish. Treat the residue with 20 ml. of water, and add 50 mg. of hydroxylamine hydrochloride. Heat on a steam bath for 10 minutes, cool, and dilute to 25 ml. with water. This solution meets the requirements of the *Heavy Metals Test*, page 763, using 20 mcg. of lead ion (Pb) and 50 mg. of hydroxylamine hydrochloride in the control (*Solution A*).

Brominated Vegetable Oil, page 90

Add the following sentence to the paragraph entitled *Free fatty acids*, page 91:

Titrate with the appropriate normality of sodium hydroxide solution, shaking vigorously, to the first permanent pink color of the same intensity as that of the neutralized alcohol, or, if the color of the sample interferes, titrate to a pH of 8.5, determined with a suitable instrument.

2-Butanone

Insert the following new monograph to precede the monograph entitled *Butyl Acetate*, page 1, *First Supplement:*

Figure 17. The Codex is continually being revised

chemical and biologic character of the additive, and the reason for its use. It must be accompanied by proof that the additive does exactly what it is said to do and that it is safe for human consumption in the long term.

On receiving a petition, which commonly runs to hundreds of pages, and even volumes, FDA experts evaluate it. First the chemists must satisfy themselves that the compound is fully and accurately described; that the manufacturing process will yield a consistently uniform product; that the additive will really do what it says it will do; and that the amount required to do so is correctly stated. The chemists also determine the amount of additive that may be expected to be found in the food in the form in which it will reach the consumer.

After the chemical review, FDA toxicologists take over. They must determine whether the additive is as safe as the petition claims. When they have finished and the agency is satisfied that the product is safe for its intended use, a regulation is drawn up and published in the Federal Register. Figure 15 shows a typical regulation.

Should anyone feel that he would be adversely affected by the regulation, he (or she) can request a public hearing. This may be followed, if necessary, by a judicial review in the U.S. Court of Appeals.

In an attempt further to ensure the safety of chemicals added to foods, a Food Chemicals Codex has been developed by the Food Protection Committee of National Academy of Sciences' National Research Council.* This is a compilation

---

*The National Academy of Sciences was created by an Act of the Thirty-seventh Congress and signed into law by Abraham Lincoln in 1863. Uniquely, it is a private organization with a federal charter. Its primary function is to bring together the most competent scientists in the country in appropriate groups to deal with scientific problems. Its great value to the

of identity specifications for food-grade chemicals. It serves as a guide for manufacturers of food chemicals so that all batches of a given chemical may be similar in character and thereby safe, because they all meet an acceptable standard.

As shown in Figure 16, the Codex specifies the means of identification and the permitted limit of impurities of each chemical it treats. The first edition of the Codex appeared in 1966, but the standards are continuously revised, and yearly supplements are issued (Figure 17). And once a chemical has been certified by the FDA for human consumption, its chemically acceptable qualities are set forth in the Codex. Thenceforth it must conform to that specification in order to be acceptable.

To answer the question posed by this chapter, food additives are as safe as it is humanly possible to make them. Because human beings are neither omniscient nor infallable that is the best we can say.

Reviewing the safety aspects of food regulations, two eminent British experts * have written:

> . . . too much or too little food is more harmful than all the additives, intentional or unintentional, likely to be found in food. There is very good evidence that infections conveyed

---

American people lies in its independence of either political or industrial control.

The Academy organized its National Research Council in 1916 when President Wilson asked its help in dealing with the scientific and technical problems created by the outbreak of World War I. The Academy has a number of other divisions to render impartial evaluation and judgment on the problems that are brought to it. One of these, the Division of Biology and Agriculture, has a Food and Nutrition Board which in turn has a Committee on Food Protection that provides facts and advice for both government and industry.

*Dr. R. F. Crampton, director of the British Industrial Biological Research Association, and Dr. P. S. Elias, Senior Medical Officer (Toxicology), Department of Health and Social Security.

to many by foodstuffs are a greater hazard than all food additives when properly used. Our food regulations, despite all their imperfections, are effective in safeguarding the health of the population against hazard from additives as long as there exists a concomitant attitude of social responsibility on the part of the food manufacturing and food distributing industry. However, regulations without controls or sanctions are worse than no regulations at all.

On the other hand, no scientist can protect the public from itself, and from the strange complexion of this age in which the obsession with absolute safety will cause people to sweep aside overriding benefits even when they entail some risk.

CHAPTER V

"In the Interests of the Consumer"

"It was not the object of our prophets and
our sages to close the gates of investigation
. . . and to prevent the mind from compre-
hending what is within its reach as is imagined
by simple and idle people, whom it suits better
to put forth their ignorance and incapacity as
wisdom and perfection, and to regard the
wisdom and distinction of others as irreligion
and imperfection, thus taking darkness for
light, and light for darkness."

MAIMONIDES

Section 401 of the Federal Food, Drug and Cosmetic Act
states that "whenever in the judgment of the Secretary such
action will promote honesty and fair dealing in the interests
of consumers, he shall promulgate regulations fixing
and establishing for any food, under its common or usual

name so far as practicable, a reasonable definition and standard of identity, a reasonable standard of quality, and/or reasonable standards of fill of container." Because the most important concept here is "the interests of consumers," the regulatory agencies have both a mandate and a responsibility to keep watch over and enforce food standards for the benefit of the public. This is as it should be, for the consumer is unable to judge for himself whether a food has been formulated, processed, packaged, and maintained as well as it could be.

Infrequently, Congress has unilaterally established a legal standard for a food. They did this for butter in 1923, by specifying that "butter shall be understood to mean the food product usually known as butter, and which is made exclusively from milk or cream, or both, with or without common salt, and with or without additional coloring matter, and contains not less than 80 per centum by weight of milk fat, all tolerances being allowed for."

Such Congressional action is the exception rather than the rule, for only two of the approximately 375 food standards presently in existence were set forth by Congress. (The other is the standard for nonfat dry milk promulgated in 1956.)

Ordinarily food standards are developed under the authority of the Food, Drug and Cosmetic Act, and are published in Title 21 of the Code of Federal Regulations. (CFR's are available in many libraries.) A standard is arrived at by negotiation after a thorough consideration of the limitations on the manufacturer and the needs and desires of the consumer. Once a food becomes legally standardized it can contain only the ingredients enumerated and only in the amounts specified. If optional ingredients are permitted, the standard requires that these be listed on the label. The mandatory ingredients, however, need not be listed. That is why Hellman's, Kraft's, Montco's, and other brands of mayonnaise, for example, have no ingredients listed on their labels. They fit the standard precisely, and contain no optional ingredients. Thus, for mayonnaise to be called mayonnaise, and not salad or French dressing, it can only contain those ingredients enumerated in the standard and in the amounts specified; anything else is not mayonnaise.

The current standard, Dressings for Foods, includes mayonnaise, French dressing, and salad dressing. Each is defined and its required and optional ingredients enumerated. Kraft's Miracle French Dressing lists the optional ingredients gum tragacanth and EDTA; its French dressing uses the optional algin and EDTA. Hellman's French Dressing lists vegetable gum and EDTA. By contrast the label on Milani's French Dressing shows no ingredients, indicating that it is formulated solely of required ingredients.

In the case of unstandardized items such as Frenchette's Low-Calorie Blue Cheese Dressing all eighteen ingredients must be specified. They include water, vinegar, blue cheese, sugar, vegetable oil, nonfat dry milk, salt, egg yolk, tragacanth, spices, imitation flavor, lactic acid, sodium benzoate, potassium sorbate, propyl paraben, calcium disodium EDTA, BHA, and BHT.

The standard for eggs and egg products covers such things as liquid, frozen, and dried eggs, yolks, whites, and combinations of these, whereas the Frozen Dessert Standard covers ice cream, ice milk, frozen custard, sherbert, and water ices. The Frozen Dessert Standard is an extreme but instructive example of how long it can take to hammer out food standards. Formal hearings were begun in 1942 and then tabled until 1946 because of World War II. Fourteen years and 40,000 pages of testimony later, a standard agreeable to all interested parties emerged. During the hearings consumer groups and industry and government representatives testified under oath about what ingredients should and should not be allowed in ice cream and what the definition of ice cream itself should be. Fortunately, all hearings on food standards do not last so long. The important point, however, is that all interested parties should be heard.

There are standards for only a fraction of the thousands

DEPARTMENT OF HEALTH, EDUCATION, AND WELFARE

Food and Drug Administration

[21 CFR Part 19]

BLUE AND GORGONZOLA CHEESE IDENTITY STANDARDS

Proposal Regarding Optional Use of Sorbic Acid and Its Potassium and Sodium Salts

Notice is given that a petition has been filed by the National Cheese Institute, Inc., 110 North Franklin Street, Chicago, Ill. 60606, proposing that the identity standards for blue cheese (21 CFR 19.565) and gorgonzola cheese (21 CFR 19.567) be amended to provide for optional application to the food surface of sorbic acid, potassium sorbate, and sodium sorbate to inhibit growth of surface mold. It is proposed that the mold inhibitors be used singly or in combination in an amount not to exceed 0.3 percent by weight, calculated as sorbic acid.

Grounds set forth in the petition are that use of the mold-inhibiting ingredients will reduce cheese losses and labor required for trimming away surface mold following the curing period, and will prevent formation of mold on retail sized cuts of cheese in distribution channels and in the hands of consumers.

The petition proposes label declaration of the proposed optional ingredients when used on either cheese.

Accordingly, it is proposed that Part 19 be amended:

1. In § 19.565 by revising paragraph (d) and redesignating it as paragraph (e) and by adding a new paragraph (d), as follows:

§ 19.565 Blue cheese; identity; label statement of optional ingredients.

*   *   *   *   *

(d) The food may have applied to its surface an optional mold-inhibiting ingredient consisting of sorbic acid, potassium sorbate, sodium sorbate, or any combination of two or more of these in an amount not to exceed 0.3 percent by weight, calculated as sorbic acid.

(e)(1) If the milk used is bleached, the label shall bear the statement "milk bleached with benzoyl peroxide."

(2) If the food contains an optional mold-inhibiting ingredient as specified in paragraph (d) of this section, the label shall bear the statement "_____ added to retard surface mold growth" or "_____ added as a preservative," the blank being filled in with the common name or names of the mold-inhibiting ingredient or ingredients used.

(3) Whenever the name of the food appears on the label so conspicuously as to be easily seen under customary conditions of purchase, the words and statements prescribed in this paragraph showing the optional ingredients used shall immediately and conspicuously precede or follow such name without intervening written, printed, or graphic matter.

Figure 18. A proposed standard as published in the Federal Register

of foods available. Prevailing opinion holds that a food selected for standardization should be one consumed by large numbers of people in fairly large quantities. Moreover, the standard must be expected to offer a clear-cut consumer benefit.

Inherent in the development of standards is a choice between possible ingredients that will result in a product with the most desirable texture, appearance, palatability, and nutritive value.

Unfortunately it is extremely difficult to obtain agreement as to what constitutes the "best" texture, taste, appearance, and so on. Certainly no two chefs, cooks, or housewives would agree on these qualities. As a result, the FDA seeks a minimum standard that all parties can agree to. This means simply that any processor can exceed the standard, but that none can offer a substandard product.

Any interested person, such as a consumer, producer, or trade association, may petition for a new standard or for an amendment to an existing one. If a petition furnishes reasonable grounds for the action, the Commissioner of the FDA will publish his proposal in the Federal Register. Figure 18 is a copy of a proposal as it appeared in the Federal Register. Moreover, the Commissioner on his own initiative may publish proposals to establish new standards or to amend existing ones.

After publishing a proposal in the Federal Register, comments and suggestions from interested parties are gathered at hearings set by the Commissioner. After evaluation of the evidence, an order is published which accepts, modifies, or rejects the original proposal. Should an interested party believe the revised proposal affects him adversely, he can request a public hearing. The order is stayed until the objection is adequately and in some instances legally adjudicated.*

Recall that Section 401 of the Drug and Cosmetic Act speaks of the interests of the consumer. Accordingly, it is vitally important that the Commissioner obtain the broadest possible consumer response to any proposed food standards. Thus it is in your interest to support and maintain consumer groups that regularly read the Federal Register to keep abreast of new proposals and provide the type of comments needed to influence the Commissioner's decision. The FDA has even at times used professional consumer opinion surveys to learn the public's views on pending proposals. The fact is that, although standards are presumed to benefit both the consumer and the producer, they are intended primarily for the benefit of the consumer. In the words of Charles C. Edwards,† Commissioner of Food and Drugs, "FDA represents that part of the health care system which provides the consumer the protection he is unable to provide for himself. . . . All of our decisions must be made in his interest after having considered all of the available scientific evidence." However, as the standards prescribe the "ground rules" that all food manufacturers must observe, the manufacturers benefit through protection from unfair competition.

That food standards are specific and inviolable was shown recently when a food processor petitioned to introduce a new product under the existing potato chip standard. The proces-

---

*For anyone interested in complete details about how standards are formulated, a bulletin entitled "Administrative Functions, Practices and Procedures," extracted from Part 2, Title 21, *Code of Federal Regulations*, Feb. 1966, is available upon request from the Department of Health, Education, and Welfare.

†From "Remarks," presented at Temple University, Philadelphia, Pennsylvania, May 5, 1970.

sor had planned to homogenize potatoes to a fine slurry, which would be fried as a continuous thin layer, then chipped. But the FDA stated that the new product would have to be labeled "artificial" since the standard clearly specifies that a potato chip must be a slice of an intact potato. The processor, realizing that such a label would jeopardize the sales of his product, has asked for a hearing to argue that "in the interest of the consumer," a chip made from homogenized potatoes is no less a chip than one made from a sliced potato.

As a result of the vastly increased demand for foreign foods and in order to provide for freer movement of foods from country to country, a new international set of food standards is currently being developed. In 1962, in response to pressure generated by participants at the joint FAO/ WHO * Conference on Food Standards a Codex Alimentarius Commission was established. As of March 1, 1969, sixty-five countries had become members of this commission. A proposed draft standard is circulated to foreign governments for their comments. After the comments have been evaluated, a "recommended standard" is adopted. This is sent to all governments for their acceptance, and at the same time is published in the Codex.

To date the United States has accepted the Codex standards for several dairy products, but with reservations, because FDA standards are generally more stringent than those developed by the CAC. For example, the United States has accepted the Codex standard, with slight differences, for butter oil. Codex standards for evaporated milk and sweetened con-

---

*Food and Agriculture Organization and World Health Organization. Both are agencies of the United Nations.

densed milk have been accepted with provision for more stringent U.S. requirements, both present and future. We have also adopted the whole milk powder standard with the proviso that neutralizers and stabilizers be excluded. The U.S. has not accepted the Codex standard for butter because it differs from the definition established by the 1923 Act of Congress.

Although Codex committees are presently working on standards for beverages, canned fruit, and vegetables, they have not yet been submitted to the U.S. for acceptance. The fact that the United States already has so many of its own food standards puts it in a strong position to guide the development of the international provisions. On the other hand, where we do not already have an operating standard, we are under heavy pressure to adopt those developed by the CAC as our own.

In addition to Federal standards and the growing list of international standards, a number of states have developed controls over imports and foods moving both inter- and intra-state. It is commonplace, for example, to read "Reg. Penna. Dept. Agr." on the labels of prepared foods. By a 1933 act of the state legislature, Pennsylvania decreed that all products made with flour would have to be "certified" if they entered the state. To obtain certification a manufacturer must prove that his premises and conditions of baking meet Pennsylvania's sanitary standards.

Although Pennsylvania does not send inspectors to other states or to foreign countries, it does require certification of the specific premises by that state or country's legally constituted health agency. It will not accept a statement from the processor. The intent of the law is to assure the consumer that all baked goods sold in Pennsylvania are from acceptable sources, but certification does not imply approval of the product itself. It merely reassures purchasers that the processing plant and its employees have met specified standards.

The notation "Reg. Penna. Dept. of Agr." appears on packages sold in states other than Pennsylvania for the convenience of the producer. It is cheaper to have all labels and packaging materials printed at one time without regard for the product's final destination.

One aspect of food standards works against the consumer's best interests. When a food becomes standardized, the manufacturer is no longer required to list the mandatory ingredients on the label. Thus the person who is hypersensitive or allergic to certain kinds of foods, particularly those containing protein, cannot know whether the standardized food is safe for him to eat. For example, the ice cream standard permits the use of egg or egg yolks (liquid, frozen, or dried) to facilitate the incorporation of air into the ice cream. Yet this ingredient is rarely noted on the cartons. It is difficult to imagine that listing all the ingredients of standardized products would be a hardship for the food processor. To do so would certainly be in the "interests of the consumer."

The history of government activity in the establishment and enforcement of food standards is as old as the human tendency to realize a little extra profit by offering an inferior product for sale. The beer testers of eighteenth-century England, who spilled a few ounces of beer on a bench and then sat on it until it dried, were the forerunners of today's analysts. If, on getting up, their leather breeches stuck to the bench, it was proof that the beer had been adulterated with sugar.

Since its enactment some 65 years ago, the Pure Food and Drug Act has attempted to prevent unacceptable food from reaching the market. With each new amendment to the Act, greater responsibility—and greater authority—for consumer protection has been vested in the FDA. As a result, the FDA has become primarily a law enforcement body whose activities have resulted in higher standards of sanitation in food plants and advanced techniques of detecting filth,* disease causing microbes, and toxic chemicals.

While these efforts have gone a long way toward assuring the cleanliness, wholesomeness, and safety of the nation's food supply, inspection and enforcement must be a continuous process because, unfortunately, a few marginal food processors and distributors are still unaware of or refuse to maintain the sanitary conditions and practices that the law demands for the protection of the consumer.

FDA inspectors make periodic unannounced visits to food plants and warehouses throughout the country. They seek to detect the presence of potentially harmful or deceptive adulterants in the product; to determine how they were introduced; if necessary, to trace a product from its distributors to its source; and to collect samples of food prior to inter- and intrastate shipment. The inspectors make thousands of visits a year to food plants that range from bakeries doing little interstate shipping to canneries whose goods can be found all over the country.

Backing up the field inspectors are teams of federal and

---

*Terms such as filth, putrid, decomposed, and contaminated are much used, particularly in legal documents. Filth refers to the presence in food of insect, animal, or human excreta, rodent hairs, and insect fragments. Putrid refers to a state of decay in which a rotting food exudes strong, unpleasant odors. Decomposed commonly denotes rotting with or without odor and is often synonymous with putrid. Contaminated is a difficult concept to describe since almost nothing is pure—not even the driven snow. It is used to define something that is impure because of its contact with a chemical or bacterial adulterant.

seizures and post office cases

SEIZURE ACTIONS charging violation of the Federal Food, Drug, and Cosmetic Act and the Federal Hazardous Substances Act are published when they are reported by the FDA District Office.

A total of 36 seizure actions to remove adulterated, misbranded, and unsafe products from the consumer market were reported in January. These included 21 seizures of foods; 3 because of poisonous and deleterious substances, and 18 because of contamination. Other seizures included 11 of drugs, 1 of medical devices, and 3 of hazardous substances.

PRODUCT, PLACE & DATE SEIZED	MANUFACTURER (M), PACKER (P), SHIPPER (S), DEALER (D)	CHARGES
FOOD / Poisonous and Deleterious Substances		
Bonemeal, digester tankage/Bucyrus, Ohio 1/2/70	Hygrade Food Products Corp./Mishawaka, Ind. (M,S)	Salmonella.
Chubs, fresh, iced/Brooklyn, N.Y. 11/6/69	Union Fisheries Corp./Chicago, Ill. (P,S)	Contain DDT, DDE, TDE, and dieldrin, pesticide chemicals not in conformity with regulations.
Egg yolks, frozen, 10% sugar/Chicago, Ill. 10/15/69	Golden Egg Products, Inc./Oneonta, Ala. (P,S)	Salmonella.
Contamination, Spoilage, Insanitary Handling		
Crab boil/Birmingham, Ala. 10/17/69	Zatarain's, Inc./Gretna, La. (M,S)	Prepared under insanitary conditions; insect contaminated; salt not declared.
Flour/Jesup, Ga. 12/8/69	Yukon Mill & Grain/Yukon, Okla. (M,S)	Prepared and packed under insanitary conditions; insect contaminated.
Gooch's Best/Council Bluffs, Iowa 12/11/69	Gooch's Feed Mill Co./Council Bluffs, Iowa (D)	Held under insanitary conditions.
Lamico Rose, Snow Lily/Stanaford, W.Va. 12/5/69	Laurinburg Milling Co./Laurinburg, N.C. (M,S)	Prepared and packed under insanitary conditions.
wheat, all purpose/Catano, P.R. 11/25/69	Molinos de Puerto Rico, Inc./Catano, P.R. (D)	Prepared, packed, and held under insanitary conditions.
Mushrooms, canned/Buffalo, N.Y. 12/17/69	Tusco Mushroom Prods., Inc./Beach City, Ohio (P,S)	Partly decomposed.
Onion rings, breaded/Lexington, Ky. 12/3/69	Moore's Seafood Products, Inc./Fort Atkinson, Wis. (M,S)	Prepared and packed under insanitary conditions; E. coli; excessive coliforms.
Wilmington, N.C. 1/2/70	Gold King Frozen Foods, Inc./Thunderbolt, Ga. (M)	"
Peanuts, medium, Virginia/Santa Fe Springs, Calif. 12/4/69	Shoemaker Candies/Santa Fe Springs, Calif. (D)	Held under insanitary conditions; rodent contaminated.
Peas, black-eyed/Mobile, Ala. 12/11/69	Cal Bean & Grain Co-op/Pixley, Calif. (P,S)	Prepared and packed under insanitary conditions.
Pecans, shelled/Kansas City, Mo. 12/31/69	Gold Kist Pecans/Canton, Miss. (P,S)	"
Salmon, pink, frozen/Seattle, Wash. 11/17/69	Mitsubishi International Corp./Valdez, Alaska (M,S)	Partly decomposed.
canned, red/Bellingham, Wash. 11/20/69	Queen Fisheries, Inc./Clark's Slough, Alaska (P,S)	Prepared and packed under insanitary conditions.
Seattle, Wash. 11/17 and 11/24/69	Kenai Packers/Kenai, Alaska (P,S)	"
Shrimp, ready-to-cook, frozen/Chicago, Ill. 12/3/69	Booth Fisheries/Brownsville, Tex. (P,S)	Partly decomposed.
Sunflower seeds, pecans, filberts, brazil nuts, in shell/New York, N.Y. 12/2/69	A. L. Bazzini Co., Inc./New York, N.Y. (D)	Held under insanitary conditions.
Walnuts/Forest Park, Ga. 12/5/69	Continental Nut Co./Chico, Calif. (P,S)	Rancid.
Wheat shorts/Nicholasville, Ky. 12/11/69	Bryan-Hunt Co./Nicholasville, Ky. (D)	Held under insanitary conditions; rodent contaminated.
DRUGS / Human Use		
DAST timekaps/Mansfield, Ohio 1/2/70	Plymouth Labs, Inc./Plymouth, Mich. (M,S)	Subpotent; lack of good manufacturing practice.
Diethylstilbestrol tablets, 5 mg./Fort Lee, N.J. 12/11/69	Strong Cobb Arner, Inc./Cleveland, Ohio (M,S)	Premature disintegration.

Figure 19. Seizure actions as published in the FDA Papers

notices of judgment

NOTICES OF JUDGMENT on Seizure Actions

FOOD / Poisonous and Deleterious Substances

Egg and/or ova products, frozen, at Columbus, M. Dist. Ga.
Charged 7-23-69; when shipped by Golden Egg Products Co., Inc., Oneonta, Ala., the articles contained **Salmonella** bacteria, **Arizona** bacteria, and decomposed eggs; [402(a)(1)], 402(a)(3). Default decree ordered destruction. **(1)**

Fishmeal, at Fernandina Beach, M. Dist. Fla.
Charged 10-22-69; when shipped by Ted Reynolds Grain Co., Houston, Tex., and Degelos Bros. Grain Co., New Orleans, La., the article contained the added poisonous and deleterious substance **Salmonella**; 402(a)(1). Consent decree authorized release to Pro-Pak Corp., Fernandina Beach, Fla., for salvaging. **(2)**

Food / Contamination, Spoilage, Insanitary Handling

Cheese, monterey jack, at Salt Lake City, Dist. Utah.
Charged 7-31-69; when shipped by C. W. and Jay Ward, Inc., Richfield, Idaho, the article, labeled in part "Banquet Better . . . Monterey Jack Cheese . . . Mfd. by Banquet Better Foods (Nelson Ricks Creamery Co.) . . . Rexburg, Idaho," contained insect filth and had been prepared and packed under insanitary conditions; 402(a)(3), 402(a)(4). Default decree authorized donation to public institution for use as animal feed. **(3)**

Citrus salad, Seald-Sweet, at Seattle, W. Dist. Wash.
Charged 8-28-69; when shipped by Seald Sweet Sales, Inc., Tampa, Fla., the article contained a decomposed substance (it was undergoing decomposition, contained viable yeast, and was in swollen and leaking containers); 402(a)(3). Default decree ordered destruction. **(4)**

Cocoa beans, at Philadelphia, E. Dist. Pa.
Charged 7-10-69; while held for sale, the article contained insect and miscellaneous filth and moldy cocoa beans; 402(a)(3). Default decree ordered destruction. **(5)**

Coconut, shredded, at Tampa, M. Dist. Fla.
Charged 8-21-69; while held by Lorenzen Coffee Service, Tampa, Fla., the article contained insect filth and was held under insanitary conditions; 402(a)(3), 402(a)(4). Default decree ordered destruction. **(6)**

Coffee beans, green, at Jacksonville, M. Dist. Fla.
Charged 7-3-69; while held by Jacksonville Port Authority, Jacksonville, Fla., the article contained insect filth, moldy beans, was partially burned, damaged by water and smoke, and was held under insanitary conditions; 402(a)(3), 402(a)(4). Consent decree authorized release to Leon Israel & Bros., Inc., New Orleans, La., for salvaging. **(7)**

Cruller mix, at Allison Park, W. Dist. Pa.
Charged 9-19-69; while held by Barkus Bakery, Allison Park, Pa., the article contained insects and had been held under insanitary conditions; 402(a)(3), 402(a)(4). Default decree ordered destruction. **(8)**

Egg yolks, frozen, at Chicago, N. Dist. Ill.
Charged 9-19-69; when shipped by Golden Egg Products Inc., Oneonta, Ala., the articles contained decomposed eggs, and one lot contained the poisonous and deleterious substance **Salmonella** organisms; 402(a)(3), 402(a)(1). Consent decree authorized release to shipper for salvaging. **(9)**

Mustard seed, at Dallas, N. Dist. Tex.
Charged 8-27-69; while held by Alford's Refrigerated Warehouse, Dallas, Tex., the articles contained rodent filth, one lot contained insect filth, and all lots were held under insanitary conditions; 402(a)(3), 402(a)(4). Consent decree authorized release to dealer for reconditioning. **(10)**

Noodles, egg, at Trevor, E. Dist. Wis.
Charged 10-13-69; when shipped by Crescent Baking Co., Davenport, Iowa, the article contained insect filth and was prepared and packed under insanitary conditions; 402(a)(3), 402(a)(4). Default decree ordered destruction. **(11)**

Onion rings, breaded, frozen, at Cincinnati, S. Dist. Ohio.
Charged 9-25-69; when shipped by Moore's Seafood Products, inc., Fort Atkinson, Wis., the article, labeled in part "Breaded Onion Rings . . . Distributed by Pierre Frozen Foods, Cincinnati, Ohio," contained **E. coli** and was prepared and packed under insanitary conditions; 402(a)(3), 402(a)(4). Default decree ordered destruction. **(12)**

Onion rings, breaded, frozen, at Mankato, Dist. Minn.
Charged 9-18-69; when shipped by Moore's Seafood Products, Inc., Fort Atkinson, Wis., the article, labeled in part "Chip Steak & Provision Co. Distributor Mankato, Minnesota . . . Breaded Onion Rings," contained **E. coli** and bacterial filth and had been prepared and packed under insanitary conditions; 402(a)(3), 402(a)(4). Consent decree ordered destruction. **(13)**

Peanuts, granulated, roasted, at Burbank, C. Dist. Calif.
Charged 9-24-69; while held by Paramount Ice Cream Corp., Burbank, Calif., the article contained rodent filth and was held under insanitary conditions; 402(a)(3), 402(a)(4). Consent decree authorized release to dealer for salvaging. **(14)**

Peanuts, granulated, roasted, at Nashville, M. Dist. Tenn.
Charged 10-1-69; when shipped by Aster Nut Products Co., Inc., Evansville, Ind., the article contained insect filth and was prepared and packed under insanitary conditions; 402(a)(3), 402(a)(4). Default decree ordered destruction. **(15)**

Peanuts, shelled, at Los Angeles, C. Dist. Calif.
Charged 6-10-69; while held by Gust Picoulas & Co., Los Angeles, Calif.,

the article contained rodent filth and was held under insanitary conditions; 402(a)(3), 402(a)(4). Default decree ordered destruction. **(16)**

FOOD / Economic and Labeling Violations

Cheese, mozzarella, at Los Angeles, C. Dist. Calif.
Charged 9-9-69; when shipped by The Danish Cheese Co., Olympia, Wash., the article lacked conformity to the standard of identity, since it contained less than 45 percent of milk fat; 403(g)(1). Consent decree authorized release to Dob Corp. Div. of Fairmont Foods of Omaha, Nebr., for salvaging. **(17)**

VITAMINS / DIETARY FOODS

Dietary supplement syrups, at Miami, S. Dist. Fla.
Charged 7-28-69; while held by Prime Pharmaceuticals, Inc., Miami, Fla., who had furnished the articles' labels, reading in part "Yodo Tanic Syrup . . . Iodine-Tannic Acid Complex in a glycerin syrup base . . . Distributed by Somar Pharmaceuticals Miami" and "Iodized Horseradish Syrup . . . Iodine-Tannic Acid Complex in a base containing Horseradish and Watercress Extracts . . . Distributed by Somar Pharmaceuticals Miami," the articles contained the nonconforming food additive iodine-tannic acid complex; 402(a)(2)(C). Default decree ordered destruction. **(18)**

Iso-Brovite vitamin tablets, at San Francisco, N. Dist. Calif.
Charged 8-15-69; while held by Broemmel Pharmaceuticals, San Francisco, Calif., who packed the article, the valuable constituents vitamin B-12 and vitamin B-1 had been in part omitted or abstracted; and label statements were false and misleading, since the article was deficient in the declared amounts of vitamin B-12 and vitamin B-1 (approx. 35 percent and 33 percent, respectively); 402(b)(1), 403(a). Default decree ordered destruction. **(19)**

Ni-Kur vitamin supplement, at Houston, S. Dist. Tex.
Charged 7-30-69; when shipped by Ni-Kur, Inc., Barberton, Ohio, the article was a new drug without an effective approved New Drug Application; the labeling contained false and misleading therapeutic claims for arthritis, bursitis, lumbago, gout, and rheumatism; and the labeling lacked adequate directions for use by laymen; 505(a), 502(a), 502(f)(1). Default decree ordered destruction. **(20)**

FOOD AND COLOR ADDITIVES

Raisins, maraschino, at Miami, S. Dist. Fla.
Charged on or about 5-12-69; when shipped by Kitchen Craft Foods Corp., Brooklyn, N.Y., the article contained the nonconforming color additive FD&C Red No. 4, and the labeling failed to declare that benzoate of soda and sulfur dioxide were chemical preservatives; 402(c), 403(k). Default decree ordered destruction. **(21)**

DRUGS / Human Use

Amphetamine combination capsules, pipenzolate combination tablets, and choline combination capsules, at Milwaukee, E. Dist. Wis.
Charged 1-21-69; while held by Formulations, Inc., Milwaukee, Wis., who manufactured the articles from ingredients shipped in interstate commerce, the articles had been prepared, packed, and held under insanitary conditions; and the circumstances of the articles' manufacture, processing, packing, and holding lacked conformity with current good manufacturing practice; 501(a)(2)(A), 501(a)(2)(B). Default decree ordered destruction. **(22)**

Aspirin-caffeine tablets and aspirin-ephedrine combination tablets, at Hialeah, S. Dist. Fla.
Charged 6-27-69; while held for sale, the articles' quality was deficient, since the aspirin in both articles was decomposed; 501(c). Default decree ordered destruction. **(23)**

Biflav-C bioflavonoid vitamin tablets, at Glendale, C. Dist. Calif.
Charged 12-28-67 and amended 5-14-68; when shipped by Lanpar Co., Dallas, Tex., the labeling on the tubes in which packets of the articles were packed contained false and misleading claims for poor tissue tone associated with weight loss, pupura, arthritis, and spontaneous abortion; the plastic bags containing the article lacked the name and place of business of the manufacturer, packer, or distributor, lacked a quantity of contents statement, and lacked the established name of each active ingredient; and the labeling of the article lacked adequate directions for use for the conditions for which the article was offered on the bulk package label, and adequate directions for such use cannot be written; 502(a), 502(b)(1,2), 502(e)(1)(A)(ii), 502(f)(1). The shipper claimed the article, and the Government moved for summary judgment. Thereafter, the court found that, although the plastic packets were in tubes labeled in part "Each tablet contains: Lemon Bioflavonoid Complex . . . 100 (or "200") mg. Vitamin C (Ascorbic Acid, U.S.P. 100 (or "200") mg. . . Lanpar Company . . . Dallas 35, Texas," that the plastic packets containing 25 tablets each were the "immediate containers" of the drugs, and that, since the plastic packets were unlabeled except for the statements "BVC-2 7555" and "BVC 8494" and since the dispensing exemption relied upon by the claimant becomes effective only at the time such drugs are actually dispensed on prescription, the articles were misbranded within the meaning of 502(b)(1,2), and 502(e)(1)(A)(ii). Accordingly, the Government was entitled to summary judgment ordering the articles condemned. The claimant filed an appeal. Pursuant to stipulation, the appeal was dismissed. Subsequently, the articles were ordered destroyed. **(24)**

Figure 20. Notices of judgment as published in the FDA Papers

state scientists capable of conducting the most sophisticated electronic and chemical analyses on samples brought in by the inspectors.

When it has been established that a food plant has not complied with the regulations, the inspector must track down the food lots suspected of being contaminated and take appropriate action.

The Food, Drug and Cosmetic Act provides for criminal prosecution, with imprisonment and fines upon conviction, seizure of goods, and injunction proceedings. Figure 19 * is a typical list of seizure actions. In Figure 20,* Notices of Judgment, the final disposition of seized items can be seen. Sometimes an item can be salvaged, but in most cases it is destroyed. It is never made available to the consumer as originally prepared.

Let us follow an inspector through a plant. First, he must review reports of previous inspections at the FDA district office. Has the plant a good record? Is it a borderline case or a chronic offender? Have promised corrections been carried out?

On arrival at the plant, the inspector is required to present his credentials and ask permission to enter. At this point, if the plant is a chronic offender, the inspector's unannounced visit can be made almost totally useless. His presence is quickly announced to the plant manager who contacts his foremen in the processing area, while the inspector is either detained at the gate or delayed on one pretext or another in the manager's office. In the interim a chemical explicitly proscribed by law can be hidden, or an unacceptable part of the plant tidied up.

---

*Notices of judgment and seizure actions are published monthly in *FDA Papers*, a publication of the Food Drug Administration.

Although it is clearly impossible to screen a sugar storage area against rodents in the time between the inspector's arrival at a plant and his appearance in the processing area, it is possible to move bags stacked on pallets to more protected areas, or conceal bags that are open or have obviously been gnawed by rats. It takes only a few moments to secrete a gallon jug of hydrogen peroxide (illicitly used to whiten fish fillets) under a few 50-pound sacks of refrigerated vegetables. Barrels of locally caught fish that are replacing their more expensive foreign "cousin" can be sealed or concealed. Hairnets that workers forget to put on and that foremen ignore can suddenly appear, and the worker with an infected finger can be "pulled" from the line and sent to rest, or assigned to other duties. Fortunately the minority of food packers who resort to these subterfuges is growing smaller every year.

Our inspector is now in the processing area. He will either choose to follow the flow of the production lines or, if he knows of a previous violation, he will check to see whether it has been corrected. He will certainly visit the raw materials' receiving and storage areas, where he will use ultraviolet or "black" light to uncover evidence of rat urine which cannot be seen by day or white light.

As he moves around the plant, the inspector will usually take samples of the product or its ingredients for analysis at the district laboratory. The tests will determine the presence of pesticide residues, food additives, insect fragments, and types and number of bacteria.

At a dairy plant, the inspector will not fail to check the raw milk for cow manure, flies, rodent hairs, or other visible particles. He will almost certainly also taste or smell some of the products to see if they have decomposed. In a fish processing plant, he will check the fish for freshness and

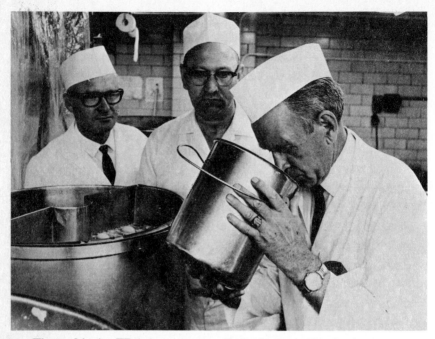

Figure 21. An FDA inspector smells broken eggs for freshness

parasitic infestation. In a bakery, his concern will be to verify that the batches of flour are free from insects or insect fragments.

Generally, however, the inspector is concerned with plant construction and layout, equipment, sanitary facilities for the work force, and the methods of operation. He will look for floors, walls, and ceilings made of materials and constructed in such a way as to defy cleaning; lighting inadequate for proper food handling; windows and doors not properly screened and barred against insects and other animals.

When examining the processing machinery the trained inspector will watch for points at which the food might become contaminated by lubricants, fuel, metal fragments, or pockets of water loaded with bacteria that can act as a source of inoculation.

He will make sure there are adequate toilets and sinks close to work areas so that the workers can wash their hands whenever necessary.

As he moves along the packing lines, the inspector will check packages and labels to ensure that they meet net weight requirements of both the FDA Act and the Fair Packaging and Labeling Act. He will verify that only permitted food additives are being used, and only in the quantities stipulated by the regulations. In addition, he will be on the alert for equipment and processing practices that might contribute to bacterial contamination. This is particularly important in products that are not heated at the end of processing so as to reduce the bacterial content to an insignificant level.*
These would include products containing eggs, milk, or cream, and particularly frozen eggs, cream-type pastries, and frozen convenience foods.

An experienced inspector will also take samples of the ice used on raw or finished products. Bacteriologic tests of the melted ice will indicate whether, against regulations, it has been made from water contaminated by feces.

The law requires that periodic inspections be made; that a report be left if insanitary practices are found; and that management be supplied with copies of all laboratory findings. Although the law only requires notification in the case of insanitary findings, the FDA has recently initiated a policy

---

*Although certain canned foods are subjected to temperatures as high as 240°F for 35 minutes, they are not sterilized. Sterilization (the complete absence of life) would produce a product unfit to eat. Consequently the heat treatment is designed to reduce microbial populations to insignificant (harmless) levels.

in which Distrct Directors notify top managment by letter
of any significant adverse findings. Then it is up to the
processor to apply whatever corrective measures he feels are
necessary. Having filed his report, the inspector's work is
done. Any legal action against the processor will be taken
by the FDA District Office. For a whimsical view of the food
processor's lot see Figure 22.

Grading is another aspect of federal inspection. While any
packer can label his product "Grade A" or "Fancy," only a
label bearing the designation U.S. Grade A gives the consumer
the assurance that the product was packed at a plant employ-
ing a fulltime federal inspector to ensure that established sanitary procedures are continuously maintained.

"YOUR TRUCK HAS BEEN RECALLED BY DETROIT,
AND YOUR CARGO HAS BEEN RECALLED BY THE FDA."

Figure 22

I'm relatively certain that when the Bard asked: "What's in a name?" he wasn't thinking about the quality of food. Nevertheless it's a pertinent question to bear in mind when shopping. For example, if a product is marked "all beef," or "all pork," it can contain no meat other than the type named. The term "meat" refers only to the muscle tissue of animals, with naturally occurring amounts of fat. If the product is labelled "all meat" it can legally contain various meats such as beef, pork, or mutton. Furthermore, the law clearly specifies that products labelled "all meat" cannot contain extenders. If extenders are used, the label must note, for example, that cereal has been added.

It may also be a good idea to notice the position of the word meat or poultry in the product name. Products called Beef and Gravy contain more meat (beef) than those labelled Gravy and Beef, and there is a lot more poultry in Turkey with Noodles than in Noodles with Turkey.

The Department of Agriculture, under whose jurisdiction this comes, requires a minimum amount of meat or poultry to be in a product before it can be called a beef or a chicken product. Chicken Noodle Soup, by way of example, must contain at least 2% chicken. A soup that contains less, must be called something else—perhaps Chicken-flavored Noodle Soup. In addition, it is now no longer considered a poultry product. Clearly, then, there is much in a name, but you do have to read the labels.

It was mentioned above that inspectors gather random samples of processed foods and their ingredients so as to have them analyzed for pesticide residues. Recently pesticide levels in the total diet have been recognized as another means of establishing the wholesomeness and safety of the food supply. Because the body burden of pesticides is primarily a function of food intake, checking isolated food samples was clearly an inadequate method of estimating an individual's total daily intake of pesticides, and a new and more sophisticated method was devised.

Attempts to develop total diet studies were reported as early as 1954, but it was not until 1967 that an acceptable plan was put forward by FAO and WHO. Their Committee on Pesticide Residues defined a total diet study as "one designed to show the pattern of pesticide residue intake by a person consuming a typical diet." While studies of this type are currently in progress in Australia, Canada, and England, it was the FDA that developed the method that all other countries now use. The U.S. agency specified that the study be based on the daily food consumption of healthy 16- to

TABLE 17
TYPICAL DAILY FOOD INTAKE OF A 16- TO 19-YEAR-OLD BOY

Breakfast:	Tomato or orange juice
	Cornflakes
	Milk
	Toast with butter and jelly
Morning snack:	1 banana
Lunch:	Grilled cheese and tomato sandwich
	Potato chips
	Pickles
	Chocolate cup cakes
	Milk
	Ice cream
After-school snack:	Cookies and milk
	(soda)
Dinner:	Beef
	Rice
	Green beans
	Tossed salad
	Fruit
	Tea, milk, or coffee

19-year-old boys—over a 14-day period. They reasoned that this age group had the most voracious appetite and consumed more food per day than any other group in the population.

An FDA study of this kind requires that foods representative of the daily consumption of the test group be purchased at retail stores in a number of cities and towns throughout the country. For this purpose Market Basket Collection centers (the name given to this operation) have been set up in Baltimore, Boston, Kansas City, Los Angeles, and Minneapolis. Each center collects one wheeled shopping cart full of food from a variety of grocery and supermarkets. The collections are made during the first week of August, October, December, February, April, and June.

The 117 foods included on the master list of items to be purchased fall into one of the following 12 groups:

I	Dairy products	VII	Root vegetables
II	Meat, fish, poultry	VIII	Garden fruits
III	Grain and cereal products	IX	Fruits
IV	Potatoes	X	Oils, fats, and shortening
V	Leafy vegetables	XI	Sugar and adjuncts
VI	Legume vegetables	XII	Beverages (including drinking water)

The foods are brought to laboratories and prepared as they would be at home. Then they are analyzed for pesticide residues. Table 17 is an example of a daily menu that might well represent the foods eaten by American boys 16 to 19 years old.

After preparation, foods are grouped according to type. Cornflakes, for example, will be stored for testing with other grain and cereal products, such as bread, crackers, rice pudding, and so forth. The milk usually added to the cereal will not be added, but instead stored with other milk products.

The amount of sugar that would normally be sprinkled over the flakes will be weighed and placed in a container to be analyzed with other products containing sugar, such as jam, jelly, and fruit cocktail. Classification and storage of all foods is accomplished before they are delivered to the chemical laboratory.

The insecticide residues most likely to be present in the above-mentioned foods fall into two major categories, the organochlorines, such as DDT, dieldrin, and lindane, and the organophosphorus compounds, such as malathion and dimethoate. A third catchall category, composed of a variety of compounds containing lead, mercury, and arsenic, is often included among the pesticides tested.

These substances find their way into food as a result of crop dusting and spraying as well as through the dipping of domestic animals to control mites, ticks, and other arthropods and insect pests.

A substance such as hexochlorobenzene could find its way into eggs via chicken feed treated to control its insect content. Residues of potassium bromide in raisins could be the result of spraying against insect infestation, whereas lead and arsenic originate in lead-arsenate sprays used to prevent incursions of insects in crops of apples and pears.

Results of total diet studies from England, Canada, Australia, and the United States indicate that so far the pesticide residues we are absorbing do not represent a health hazard. They are well below the acceptable daily intake levels established by the FAO/WHO committee.

In this regard, a statement * by Dale R. Lindsay, Associate Commissioner for Science, FDA, is particularly pertinent.

---

*He was addressing the 61st Annual Convention of the Flavor and Extract Manufacturers Association held at Boca Raton, Florida, May 4, 1970.

"We started 25 years too late to keep DDT out of the environment," he said; "we can identify and document a long list of adverse effects it produces in the environment, and for this reason there is justification for banning it, but we are still looking for its adverse effects upon man himself at the levels he encounters normally."

A little more than a month later, chemical contaminants in foods was the subject of a symposium in Canada, sponsored by the Canadian Department of National Health and Welfare. One of the reports * stated that as far as human beings are concerned "the dietary intake of the major pesticides has not increased in recent years—if anything it has shown a decline." The researchers went on to say that "while most investigators still hold to the theory that the absorption of pesticides via foods is the primary and the most significant one, we believe it is the home and garden use of pesticides that is responsible for the more than minimal pesticide concentrations found in the tissues of the members of the general population. . . . We believe that the time has come to recognize that in a large segment of the population the diet is not necessarily the prime source of the pesticides found in human tissues, and that the intake above the truly minimal doses absorbed with food permitted in interstate commerce is largely avoidable." One of their conclusions was: "The ingestion of the minimal amounts of organochlorine pesticides in the diet of FDA-controlled food products presents no hazard to human health and longevity. Available evidence indicates that residues of the organophosphates and carbamates in use today are insignificant and present no problem as

---

*Delivered by Dr. W. B. Deichmann and Dr. W. E. MacDonald of the Department of Pharmacology and the Research and Teaching Center of Toxicology, University of Miami School of Medicine.

contaminants of marketed FDA-controlled food products, including fruit and vegetables."

The heart of the FDA operation is the voluntary compliance of the food industry with the regulations that have been established. Indeed, the more enlightened processors have long practiced a kind of self-regulation that includes self-inspection of plant, materials, and production procedures, and maintenance of good manufacturing practices aimed at assuring the manufacturer of FDA approval and protecting the interests of the consumer.

As long ago as 1937, the salmon industry instituted a Better Salmon Control Program to improve the quality of its product and to prevent inferior salmon from reaching the consumer. In 1946 the American Baking Institute initated an industry-wide program of plant inspection, personnel training, and standardization of equipment to improve in-plant sanitation. Since then self-regulatory programs have been adopted by the Dried Fruit Association, the National Association of Frozen Food Packers, and the national associations of shrimp breeders, pecan shellers, and canners.

Moreover, there is a concerted move within the FDA to establish a kind of Bible of good manufacturing practices for the entire food industry. This would allow each processor to gauge for himself whether he was following the type of practices destined to ensure a continuous supply of wholesome food to the consumer.

Considering the existence of food standards at federal, state, and international levels, nationwide inspection by a well-trained force of dedicated men, and a growing trend toward self-regulation via a set of good manufacturing practices, the American consumer can be reassured that for the most part the food available to him is safe, wholesome, and nutritious.

TABLE 18
CHRONOLOGY OF FOOD PROTECTION LEGISLATION

Ever since the establishment of organized communities people have been concerned about adulteration of food and drink.

As early as 1202 King John (of Magna Carta fame) enacted the first food law, the Assize of Bread. This prohibited the substitution of such ingredients as ground peas or beans for flour.

1784	Massachusetts enacted the first general food law in the United States. "An act against selling unwholesome Provisions" decreed stiff penalties for knowingly selling "diseased, corrupted, contagious or unwholesome provisions"—both food and drink.
1824	Flour Inspection Act of Alexandria, Virginia (then in the District of Columbia), passed.
1850	California passed a pure food and drink law.
1891–1895	Acts passed requiring inspection of animals for disease before slaughter.
1897	March 2. The Tea Importation Act was passed, providing for inspection of all tea entering U.S. ports.
1906	June 30. The original Food and Drug Act was passed. The Meat Inspection Act was passed the same day, requiring that all meat shipped in interstate commerce be inspected.
1913	March 3. Gould Amendment enacted, requiring that a definite quantity of information appear on food packages.
1916	The Grain Standards Act was passed. It established standards for grain shipped in interstate commerce.
1923	March 4. Filled Milk Act prohibited interstate traffic in milk or cream containing any fat other than milk fat.
1927	Import Milk Act was passed. It decreed that imported milk must meet domestic minimum standards.
1930	McNary-Mapes Amendment was enacted, authorizing standards of quality and fill of container for canned food.
1938	The Federal Food, Drug and Cosmetic Act amended.
1939	July 14. First Federal food standards issued (for canned whole tomatoes, tomato puree, and tomato paste).
1946	Agricultural Marketing Act was enacted. It established standards for a number of foods not covered by other laws.
1956	Fish and Wildlife Act was passed, setting standards for fish and shellfish.

1956   Nonfat Dry Milk Act was passed. It was the second food to be defined by Congress. The Act set standards of identity for nonfat dry milk.

1957   The Poultry Products Inspection Act was passed, requiring ante and post mortem inspection of the animals, inspection of the sanitary standards of the processing personnel, and plant maintenance.

1967   Wholesome Meat Act enacted. It authorized the Secretary of Agriculture to aid the states in implementing inspection programs.

CHAPTER VI

Foods in our Future

"Feed me with food convenient to me."

ECCLESIASTES

It might not be too farfetched, in fact, in the world of 1985 it might be commonplace for people to pop food tablets into their mouths rather than take time out for a meal.

For example, a busy breadwinner or shopper, finding no time for a proper sit-down leisurely lunch, could reach into a pocket or handbag and take out a packet of lozenge-like tablets. Each tablet, the size of a quarter or smaller, with a variety of flavors and nutritional characteristics could supply nutrients equivalent to a balanced meal or perhaps just a snack to tide one over until a normal meal could be obtained.

It doesn't require too great an imagination to envision these tablets providing nutrients equivalent to fish and chips, steak and potatoes, or ham and eggs. Fortunately or unfortunately, although such tablets are not yet available, there are a number of other developments that will surely affect eating patterns.

For more than 20 years we have been reading reports about the imminence of irradiated foods. But each report has immediately been countered by another indicating the possible health hazards of irradiation. It does appear, though, that within this decade we will see an expanded use of this technique.

Irradiation is the first entirely new method of preserving food since the French confectioner François Nicolas Appert discovered thermal processing in 1809.*

Among the first to become interested in preservation by irradiation was the U.S. Navy. The perishability of fresh vegetables and the desire to reduce refrigeration facilites aboard ship caused the Navy to award a contract to the Massachusetts Institute of Technology in 1948 to further explore the possible benefits of ionizing radiation.

Irradiation is a particularly attractive solution for preserving foods such as oranges, strawberries, fish, potatoes, and other vegetables that would be altered by cooking or refrigeration. Many of these are foods high in moisture and thus subject to swift bacterial decomposition. Low-dose irradiation does not kill all the bacteria, but it so reduces their levels that the food will not spoil for an extended period. This limited treatment of foods is called radiation "pasteurization" and it does not alter taste, odor, or cooking characteristics. Oranges and potatoes irradiated in this way will stay fresh for more than two months when maintained at about 45 de-

---

*In 1795, Napoleon, knowing that an army "travels on its stomach," offered 12,000 francs for a new way of preserving food. Appert won the prize by placing food in wide-mouthed bottles, corking them, and then heating the bottles in a water bath. The existence of bacteria was not known at the time, but Appert correctly surmised that the application of heat would aid in food preservation.

TABLE 19
IRRADIATION DOSE RANGE REQUIRED FOR VARIOUS FOOD
PRESERVATION PROCESSES

Process	Rads
Inhibition of sprouting; carrots, onions, potatoes	4,000–40,000
Inactivation of trichina tapeworm—*Trichinella spiralis*	30,000–60,000
Destruction of grain- and cereal-infesting insects	1000,000–500,000
Sterilization of food (removal of all microbes)	2,000,000–5,000,000
Inactivation of enzymes (protein molecules)	Up to 10,000,000

grees, which is just a little warmer than most home refrigerators. Figure 23 shows the result of such treatment.

The required dose of radiation increases sharply with each lower form of life or biological process that must be destroyed, as Table 19 shows.

Under the Food, Drug and Cosmetic Act of 1958, ionizing radiation was defined as a food additive. Accordingly, it must be shown to be safe for its intended use before it can be certified. In 1966, the FDA certified irradiated canned bacon, white potatoes, wheat, and wheat flour as safe for human consumption. Then in 1968, certification for the bacon was withdrawn. However, considering the current political climate in the U.S. and the entrance of politics into heretofore professional territory, FDA certification of a longer list of irradiated products may be some time in coming.

Interestingly enough, the USSR with its particularly limited use of food additives permits the unrestricted use of irradiated fresh fruits and vegetables, dried fruits, grains, and potatoes.

Figure 23. Effects of irradiation on oranges and potatoes

And it is of more than passing interest that fish preserved by radiation may soon go on sale in England. The report of the Atomic Energy Authority of the United Kingdom for the year ending March 31, 1970 states that the Authority developed techniques for bombarding fish and imported frozen meat pet foods with controlled doses of cobalt rays. Such irradiated food was fed to animals for six years with no ill effects.

Apparently irradiation of beer proved unsuccessful. Dr. Walter Marshall, Director of the Harwell Research Group, said that "the tests were dreadful." Only one of 12 guinea pigs liked the taste.

Politics, too, is responsible for nearly a quarter of a century of delay in introducing whole fish protein concentrate (FPC) in any significant quantities into the United States. Both the process and the end product are still accepted here only with reservations.

FPC is the result of extracting oils and fats from whole fish, then drying and grinding the high-protein residue into a fine powder. Because of the ready availability of tremendous tonnages of nonfood fish (often called "trash fish"), it was hoped that FPC would become the ideal low cost protein supplement for the substandard diets on which millions subsist around the world. Unfortunately more than two decades have slipped by in bureaucratic wrangling over whether a product made of whole fish—head, viscera, skin, and bones —is esthetically suitable or not.*

*Protein deficiency is a staggering world problem. During the 1968 Olympic tryouts in India officials found that not a single Indian athlete met the minimum qualifying standards for any of the track and field events. And yet we haggle over whether FPC is wholesome for human consumption. Clearly our sense of values has gone awry.

The FDA has now approved for human consumption a deodorized food-grade FPC (a nondeodorized version for animal feed is also available), but only with reservations. The agency has stipulated that only red hake and such hake-like fish as Alaska pollock, menhaden, and some herring species may be used because toxologic data have shown them to be safe for humans. Anchovies, for example, may not be used, not because they are inherently dangerous, but simply because toxicologic data has not been obtained for them. In fact the FDA has required that toxologic tests be made on each species of fish that manufacturers contemplate using, even though many species are similar in feeding habits.

The FDA has designated FPC a direct food additive and subject to the controls covering all food additives. However, the ruling specifies that FPC is intended for use only in homes, and may not be sold in packages weighing more than one pound. These limitations were ostensibly made to prevent food products containing FPC from being compounded on a commercial scale, so as to "protect" those people who would be offended by eating a product that included a derivative of whole fish. This atttude, of course, vitiates the original intention of making a high-quality protein widely available at low cost.

Chile has had the most experience with FPC, and has found it to be a particularly wholesome and beneficial source of high-quality animal protein for school and hospital meals.

At this writing, three companies are readying powdered FPC products for the market. They are Cardinal Protein of Nova Scotia, Alpine Marine Protein Industries, Inc., of New Bedford, Massachusetts, and Astia of Sweden (in partnership with Nabisco-Astia Nutrition Corporation). The Astia product will use only eviscerated fish.

Alpine's product, Instant Protein, will be available in half ounce packets to blend with each cup of flour, before proceeding as usual to make brownies, cakes, breads, rolls, corn muffins, tortillas, and pancakes. Alpine also claims that their product blends well with mashed yams and potatoes, corn fritters, potato pancakes, and spaghetti sauce.

Each packet provides the protein equivalent of two eggs, or 4 ounces of fresh fish, or 2.5 ounces of beefsteak. It has the consistency and sun-tanned color of face powder, and can be stored without refrigeration for months. This should make it uniquely suitable for tropical and subtropical areas where high-protein foods normally spoil rapidly.

Hopefully intransigent regulatory officials in the U.S. will give way before long and make FPC freely available in bulk here as it already is in Canada.

The venerable soybean that has nourished men for more than four millenia may also yield some of the most promising foods of the future. The fantastic protein content of soybeans is, pound for pound, four times that of eggs, fifteen times that of milk, twice that of chicken, three times that of lamb, and two and a half times that of beef. Equally important, soybean protein is a complete high-quality protein.* Unfortunately, most Occidental methods of preparing soybeans have little to recommend them. When cooked whole, they require from 3 to 4 hours to soften and even then are bitter

---

*On reaching the gut, proteins are split or hydrolyzed, with the consequent release of their complement of amino acids. Analysis of the hydrolysates shows that all proteins do not yield the same types or amounts of amino acids. Accordingly, it is now well established that different proteins possess different physiologic or biologic value. A sampling of common foods and their approximate biologic values are: whole egg protein, 95; milk, 90; meat protein, 75; cereal proteins, 55; white flour, 50. By way of comparison, cooked soybean has a value of 75.

and indigestible. The Chinese, having used soybeans for thousands of years, do better. Usually they mash the softened beans together with gypsum (calcium sulfate) to form a curd or semiliquid. This is allowed to undergo a bacterial or fungal fermentation to produce tofu and natto, two cheeselike products. However, neither the results nor the long preparation time have appealed to Westerners.

During World War II, a mealy sort of soybean flour was developed in the United States. It contained a high proportion of hulls and had an unpleasant "beany" flavor. Processors then toasted the flour to disguise the beany taste with an equally unacceptable burnt taste. To make matters worse, heating often denatured the protein. The ill-considered use of soybean "flour" as a response to wartime shortages has left many people with a poor opinion of it.

Since World War II, soybean technology has undergone a revolution. One of the most startling developments is the production of edible soy-protein fibers that are spun on conventional textile equipment and then processed into any kind of "meat" desired. Textured Edi-Pro, made by the Ralston Purina Company, is shown in Figure 24. The tasteless, orderless fibers resemble silky blonde hair. Figure 25 shows the tensile strength of the fibers being measured.

To make the fibers the beans are first treated with mild alkali to extract the protein. They are then extruded through thousands of tiny holes in a platinum spinner and put into a coagulating bath where fiber formation occurs. During the extrusion and coagulating processes the diameter of the fibers can be varied from 0.001 to 0.030 inch so that the result will be anything from delicate fibrils to tough strands. At the same time the lay of the fibers can be regulated. A random

Figure 24. Ralston Purina's Edi-Pro, magnified many times

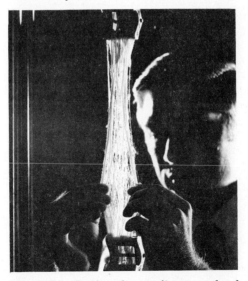

Figure 25. Testing the tensile strength of Edi-Pro

TABLE 20

TYPICAL ANALYSES OF A VARIETY OF WORTHINGTON AND BATTLE CREEK PRODUCTS

Product	Serving	Protein grams	Fat grams	Carbo-hydrate grams	Ash grams	Fiber grams	Mois-ture grams	Calo-ries
Big Pat (burger)	100 grams	21.8	8.0	16.6	2.6	0.4	50.6	226
	1 pat=71 grams	15.5	5.7	11.8	1.8	0.3	35.9	160
Frysticks (drained)	100 grams	16.2	4.6	6.9	2.2	0.8	69.3	134
	1 Frystick=64 grams	10.4	2.9	4.4	1.4	0.5	44.3	85
Numete	100 grams	13.1	16.9	11.1	2.7	0.9	55.3	249
	½-in. slice=65 grams	8.5	11.0	7.2	1.8	0.5	35.8	161
Vegetarian Cutlets	100 grams	15.1	1.5	2.8	1.4	0.1	79.1	85
	1 slice=36 grams	5.4	0.5	1.0	1.0	0.03	28.5	30
Chicken Style Sliced	100 grams	21.4	18.5	2.7	2.6	2.6	54.8	263
	1 slice=1 ounce	6.1	5.2	0.8	0.7	0.7	15.5	75
Beef Style Roll & Sliced	100 grams	21.3	10.4	5.5	1.6	0.1	61.3	201
	1 slice=1 ounce	6.0	3.0	1.6	0.5	0.01	17.4	57
Salisbury Steak Style	100 grams	18.0	13.0	10.8	3.5	0.15	54.7	232
	1 slice (2 ounce) = 56.7 grams	10.2	7.4	6.1	1.9	0.08	31.0	131
Fried Chicken Style	100 grams	10.7	8.0	4.4	1.7	0.07	75.3	132
	1/5 can=74 grams	7.8	5.9	3.2	1.2	0.05	54.9	97

Food	Serving							
Beef Style	100 grams	10.2	5.4	5.0	1.5	0.02	77.9	109
w/ Gravy	1/6 can=65 grams	6.6	3.5	3.3	1.0	0.01	50.6	71
Veja Links	100 grams	15.6	15.0	5.2	1.1	0.05	63.1	218
	2 links=52 grams	8.1	7.8	2.7	0.6	0.03	32.8	113
Vegetable	100 grams	14.6	0.6	2.7	1.7	0.2	80.2	75
Skallops	4–5 pieces=70 grams	10.2	0.4	1.9	1.2	0.1	56.1	53
Vegetable	100 grams	14.9	0.8	4.7	0.2	0.2	79.2	86
Steaks	3–4 pieces=70 grams	10.4	0.5	3.3	0.1	0.1	55.4	59
Smoked Beef	100 grams	21.3	7.7	11.6	4.0	0.17	55.3	201
	4 slices=1 ounce	6.0	2.2	3.3	1.2	0.05	15.7	57
Turkey Style	100 grams	20.2	15.9	6.7	2.8	0.26	54.3	251
	2 slices=1 ounce	5.7	4.5	2.0	0.8	0.07	15.4	71

mat, for example, will yield a "ham" loaf, while laying the fibers parallel to one another will make the resulting "meat" more chewy. Coloring and flavoring are then added to simulate chicken, beef, sausage, or turkey, and the products are then molded to the desired shape. Figure 26 shows Worthington Foods's simulated bacon and sausage before and after cooking. Table 20 indicates the nutritional values of their Fibrotein spun protein products, and Table 21 shows comparative values for a number of common foods. From a perusal of these two tables, it is clear that the made-up items —some call them meat analogs—are nutritionally equal to or better than the best natural products. In fact, people concerned about high cholesterol and calories should find these items intriguing. Stripple, a spun protein "bacon," for example, has only 16 calories per slice as compared to some 50 for

Figure 26. Worthington Foods's simulated bacon and sausage meat before and after sautéing

TABLE 21
NUTRIENTS IN COMMON FOODS

Food Item	Protein grams	Fat grams	Carbo- hydrate grams	Moisture grams	Calories
Whole milk—1 cup (8 ounces)	9	10	12	87	165
Creamed cottage cheese (100 grams)	12	3	3	78	90
Eggs—boiled (2)	12	6	—	74	160
Hamburger patty— lean (100 grams)	23	10	—	60	185
Lamb chops—lean and fat (100 grams)	24	39	—	44	450
Shrimp, canned (100 grams)	23	1	—	66	150
Peanuts, roasted (1 cup)	39	71	28	2	840

the real thing. These foods are less expensive to produce than the natural product; they do not shrink on cooking; and they are much easier to prepare. Moreover, they are reasonably close to the natural products in taste.

If they live up to the manufacturers' claims, these products could be a treat for people who have been on bland, meatless, or low-meat diets for an extended period. They could prove interesting to the hospital dietician faced with the problem of varying menus for the sick, and they might be a godsend to vegetarians and those whose diets are limited by their religion. Present indications are that these products will be on the shelves of many markets within the next few years.

Even sooner we shall be offered a most imaginative instant breakfast that will incorporate the "bacon" made of spun soybean fiber. The "bacon" will be dehydrated, diced and mixed with bread batter. After baking the loaves will be sliced, dipped in egg batter, frozen, and packaged. The consumer will simply pop a slice in his toaster for the simplest possible bacon and egg breakfast. As the Prophet said, "What man can conceive, man can create."

Already in selected test markets around the country is a Pillsbury product called Space Food Sticks. Developed with the aid of some of the food technology that made the Apollo moon missions possible, these balanced nutrient snacks are a mixture of vegetable oil, carbohydrate, flavoring, vitamins, and minerals coated with sodium caseinate, a protein. Although they offer a good balance of calories and nutrients, it will be up to the consumer to decide their future.

Protein from petroleum? Even that may be a commonplace in the supermarkets of the 1980's. Oil companies have long known that microbes can grow on a diet of crude oil. Bacteria and fungi are often found growing on the bottom of oil storage tanks, in oil-impregnated soils, and even under

TABLE 22
GROWTH RATES

Species	Doubling time
Bacteria	3–5 hours
Soy beans	1–2 weeks
Chickens	2–4 weeks
Cows	2–4 months

tar-surfaced roads. But it was not until 1952 that the companies began to investigate the possibility of increasing the food supply from this nuisance. In that year Felix Just, a German biologist, published an account of his successful attempt to grow yeast cells on a diet of paraffin. It was the first time this had been done, and it aroused immediate interest, for yeast, like other single-celled microbes, simply divide and divide as long as they have a suitable supply of food. Yeast and bacteria can be viewed as sophisticated food processing plants that first produce amino acids from an oxygen-enriched solution of hydrocarbons and minerals. They then use these amino acids as building blocks to synthesize proteins. By manipulating the conditions of growth, the microbes can be made to yield as much as 70 percent of their weight in high-quality protein.

As the population grows and land becomes scarcer, raising meat animals is a more and more expensive way of producing protein. For example, a 1000-pound steer can produce about 1 pound of usable protein a day, while 1000 pounds of bacteria can produce 4000 pounds of usable protein in the same length of time. Moreover, the bacteria can be grown in tanks without soil, sunlight, rain, or a labor force to look after them. Table 22 shows the time needed by four protein sources to double in weight.

British Petroleum has been operating a pilot proteins-from-petroleum plant at Lavera, France, since 1963, and today there is hardly an oil company that has not entered the lists. Some companies are experimenting with bacteria; others with yeast. They are fattening them on crude oil paraffin, methane, gas-oil, natural gas, carbon dioxide, even a slurry made of old newspapers.* The U.S. Bureau of Mines is trying out low-grade coal in its tests. The microbe crops are then filtered and put through a centrifuge, among other steps, before they

---

*An aqueous slurry of shredded newspaper, interestingly enough, contains a respectable diet for microbes and can be converted into SCP thereby providing much needed protein and at the same time removing a major source of waste. This of course is the epitome of recycling.

are dried to an edible, tasteless, odorless white powder (or flake) now known as SCP (single-cell protein).

Chemical analysis has shown the powder to consist of between 50 to 70 percent protein that is rich in many of the amino acids lacking in common food plants. This single-cell protein could be blended with many foods—flour, soup mixes, beverages—to increase their nutritional value, and its relatively low cost would make it more than competitive with other protein sources.

A by-product of SCP manufacture is the upgrading of fuel oil. Much of the oil on which the microbes dine is low-grade crude, which contains a high level of paraffin waxes. As they grow, the microbes use up much of the wax leaving a more refined oil that can be used as a No. 2 fuel oil, suitable for both domestic heating and diesel engines. Although No. 2 fuel oil is not in great demand in the U.S., it is much used in European countries.

Glancing back to the discussion of spun vegetable protein (SVP), it is easy to see a possible marriage between it and SCP; develop the first and have an unlimited source for the second. No doubt that SVP users are keeping a careful watch on developments in the SCP field.*

My own hope is that cows will not become entirely obsolete, for one cannot help but wonder if an "oil-fed" steak would inspire a Brillat-Savarin of the future to new culinary and gastronomic heights.

---

*The use of SCP as a base for SVP products would probably depend on the procedure used to obtain the microbial protein. If the process did not coagulate the protein I could see no difficulty. If it did, it would no longer be suitable for spinning.

CHAPTER VII

A Point of View

"Strongly held opinions often determine what
kind of facts people are able or willing to
perceive."

ROBERT WAELDER
Progress and Revolution, 1967

The despondency of whole nations is a cyclical phenomenon
in history. For the most part, these periods are marked by
their sense of helplessness and impending doom. The world
is in the midst of just such a period now, and some people
are blaming the changes brought about by science and
scientists. Sir Peter Medawar summed it up brilliantly in his
presidential address to the British Association for the Advancement of Science:

> Once again we are oppressed by a sense of decay and
> deterioration, but this time, in part at least, by a fear of the
> deterioration of the world through technological innovation.
> Artificial fertilizers and pesticides are undermining our health

(we tell ourselves), soil and sea are being poisoned by chemical and radioactive wastes, drugs substitute one kind of disease for another, and modern man is under the influence of stimulants whenever he is not under the influence of sedatives. Once again there is a feeling of despondency and incompleteness, a sense of doubt about the adequacy of man, amounting in all to what a future historian might again describe as a failure of nerve. Intelligent and learned men may again seek comfort in an elevated kind of barminess (but something kind and gentle nevertheless). Mystical syntheses between science and religion like the Cambridge Neo-Platonism of the mid-seventeenth century have their counterpart today, perhaps, in the writings and cult of Teilhard de Chardin and in a revival of faith in the Wisdom of the East. Once again there is rootlessness or ambivalence about philosophical thinking, as if the discovery or rediscovery of the insufficiency of reason had given a paradoxical validity to nonsense.*

A number of factors are responsible for this state of mind in the United States. One is the growing dislike for science and scientists. Here again the long history of contributions to life and health made by science and its handmaiden, technology, to the vast improvement of the human condition is either ignored or forgotten. And again the question must be raised. How is it possible that given the increased life span—great numbers living to and beyond the biblical injunction of "four score and ten"—the fact that life has never been healthier, and the fact that comfort and ease have been attained by so many, how is it possible that scientists are falling from grace?

On this score, a provocative and reasonable hypothesis to account for this widespread and growing attitude was put

*"The Effecting of All Things Possible," delivered before the Association on September 3, 1969, at Exeter, England.

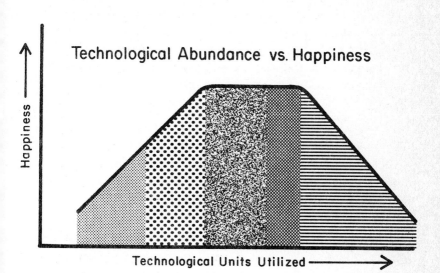

Figure 27

forth by Professor Meredith Thring of the Imperial College, London, in the form of the graph in Figure 27.*

The horizontal axis of the graph, following the arrow, indicates increasing technology; the vertical, also following the direction of an arrow, indicates increasing happiness.

Initially, happiness and technological advancement are directly related; increased technological advancement brings increased happiness. The introduction of sanitary water sup-

---

*Professor Thring's view was brought to the United States by Dr. Magnus Pike, President of the Institute of Food Science and Technology of the United Kingdom, and was presented in his keynote speech at the General Session of the Annual Meeting of the Institute of Food Technology, May 25, 1970, San Francisco.

plies, sewage disposal systems, electricity, soap, pasteurized milk, inspected meat, unadulterated bread, each progressively adds to human happiness. After this period of courtship and romance, the union is taken for granted—increased technology elicits no increase in happiness. That this goes on for a time is represented by the flat or plateau portion of the curve.

This period is followed by a descent: disenchantment with technology—too much of a good thing. Technology with its abundance has increased too far. Too many automobiles, airplanes, TV sets; too much DDT and perhaps altogether too much convenience, including the many instant foods.

Scientists may be guilty of having taken their work too seriously and having done their job too well. But scientists have also been their own worst enemy.

For too long food scientists, technologists, chemists, and nutritionists have been talking to one another as though the public at large didn't exist. Toxicologists and pharmacologists have not written a word of encouragement for the consumer. The scientists have been content to talk only to each other, while the nonscientists have been allowed to "educate" the public. As a result the American consumer, deluged with conflicting opinions masquerading as facts, is confused and resentful. Although our food supply has never in history been more abundant, varied, or safe, the consumer is running scared.

Scientists have simply attended their meetings, read their papers, and gone home, satisfied that they have done a good day's work. This is patently unsatisfactory. We have done a deplorable job of presenting our story to the general public. It is time that we speak and write for that public rather than confine ourselves solely to our professional forums, leaving the larger field to muckrakers with their purple prose and un-

tutored amateurs who cry "poison." Both independent scientists at universities and not so independent scientists working
for the government are guilty of having failed to adequately
inform the public of the work they are doing to help that
very same public.

Nonscientists have been less reticent. Late in July, 1970,
for example, a symposium in London explored "The Threats
and Promises of Science." The subject is a worthy one, for
we are all aware that the automobile is both a convenience
and a killer, and that the scalpel can be used for murder as
well as for surgery. However, one of the participants *
hardly contributed to the advancement of public enlighten-
ment when he asked the rhetorical question: "In America
there are 3000 different additives put into foodstuffs. The only
formal research that has been done into them is that none
of them on their own will kill you. Has anybody bothered to
find out what happened when two or more of them are
mixed?" He went on to state that "when an accident happens
one of the additives is merely taken off the market."

The speaker had simply not bothered to inform himself
about food additive testing. If he had, he would have discovered that total diet studies are performed on a variety of
animals and in some cases on human volunteers to test the
safety of the complete range of additives consumed together.
His second statement is equally erroneous, if I am correct
in assuming that by "accident" he means the accidental use
of too much of a permitted additive in a given batch of food.
In such a case, the contaminated batch of food would be
taken off the market, but the use of the additive would not

---

*Allen Zaretzky, assistant professor of Social Welfare at the State Uni-
versity of New York, Buffalo. He has a master's degree in social work. The
quotations are taken from the London *Sunday Telegraph* of July 28, 1970.

be barred, any more than a drug would be barred because one doctor accidentally administered an overdose. But then, had Professor Zaretzky done his research before he spoke, his comments might well not have been quoted in the *Sunday Telegraph*. Again I must point to scientists and say that, had they done the job of education needed, nonscientists would not be getting newspaper publicity for their erroneous and harmful messages. And the general public would be less fearful, perhaps even eager to accept new ideas. One of the strangest paradoxes of our time is that in this age of science the scientific sophistication of the general population is abysmal. For a civilization so dependent upon science and technology, Americans are scientific illiterates.

This popular atmosphere of negativism toward science and scientists notwithstanding, no such attitude prevails with respect to reading about new scientific developments. In fact there is almost a hunger for new and startling discoveries, which are now regularly featured in newspapers and on radio and TV.

Unfortunately too many science writers or reporters of science fail to explain, in the course of a daily column or television show, that the items being described are usually only preliminary findings which for the most part remain to be repeated, substantiated, or reproduced by the original investigator or other scientists in other parts of the country or world. It is this lack of understanding and the appreciation of its implications that misleads the public. As a consequence readers are often confused and bewildered by conflicting statements, and by what appears to be evident differences of opinion between and among scientists.

Again unfortunately, most readers do not appreciate that

differences of opinion are what makes science "tick." Differences * force scientists to constantly check and re-check their procedures, data, and conclusions. And there is no subject on which the "books" are ever closed or investigations "finally" completed. Rather all subjects are subject to periodic review and evaluation as new tools and theories become available.

Consequently, I would appeal for two things: when reading news of developments emanating from some laboratory or some one investigator, do so with the reservation that what is being reported is a new finding subject to much review and revision before it will become accepted doctrine; secondly, I appeal to popular writers not only to indicate in their columns the implications of the work they are describing, but to clearly indicate that the work is new and needs substantiation before it can even be considered as remotely relevant or reliable.

Politicians too have gotten into the act, for they have realized that our food supply is a sensitive, vote-getting issue that will almost guarantee them wide exposure in the press. They have been able to take the decision-making process away from the professional scientists and bring it into the political arena where decisions are at the mercy of the alliance of political power. The cyclamate fiasco is an excellent example of a political decision coupled with the release to the

---

*Differences can arise as a result of one investigator using mice while another uses rabbits or dogs. Some investigators may use too few animals or only animals of one sex, or they may keep an experiment going for three months while another's goes on for a year. Differences may also arise because different concentrations of a chemical were administered; dissimilar sites for introducing the chemical were also employed. And the controls, the untreated groups, may be improperly selected and maintained.

press of premature laboratory findings.* Based on data obtained by injecting massive doses into laboratory rats, cyclamates were banned from food and drink as of January 1, 1970. Then, in June of the same year, Dr. Charles C. Edwards, Commissioner of the FDA, announced that he would convene a medical advisory group to reconsider the regulation. However, two months later, cyclamates were banned without the benefit of deliberations by the medical advisory group. Perhaps another reversal of position can be expected shortly.

Although made "in the best interests of the consumer," such conflicting decisions leave the consumer not only skeptical, but anxiety ridden. Indeed, he can be excused if he finds something of an incredibility gap here.

The recent fright about mercury in tuna fish must be some sort of peak of official irresponsibility. In banner headlines and in radio and television announcements we were told that canned tuna was "contaminated" (itself an inflammatory word given to multiple interpretations depending on one's personal psychological needs). The FDA by its own admission had set an arbitrary limit to the level of mercury that it would tolerate in fish. They then removed over one million cans of tuna from market shelves because samplings showed that a small percentage of them contained fish that exceeded the mercury level they had set as acceptable. At the same

---

*Even scientists recognize the latter danger. When scientific findings are published prematurely "personal ambition for recognition has clearly outstripped the cooler judgment of awaiting more definitive data," wrote Dr. Francis D. Moore, Mosely Professor of Surgery at the Harvard Medical School and Surgeon in Chief at the Peter Bent Brigham Hospital in Boston. His subject was "Therapeutic Innovation: Ethical Boundaries in the Inital Clinical Trials of New Drugs and Surgical Procedures." The article appeared in *CA*, pp. 213–23, July–August, 1970.

time the FDA assured consumers that the cans that had been seized presented no hazard to our health. But what was the consumer to think of the contradiction? The nonhazardous tuna was taken off the shelves.

Furthermore, we were told that fish canned as long ago as 1927 had levels of mercury as high as or higher than fish canned yesterday, and that the implication of this remarkable observation was unknown. Again, fill in the blanks as you will.

To add fuel to a situation already containing more heat than light, Minamata disease was mentioned in each day's tuna fish story in the newspapers. Again and again we were told of the crippling and fatal effects of the mercury found in shellfish that had been eaten in Minamata, Japan, in the 1950's, and then were left to our own devices to link or not to link— again according to individual psychological needs—Minamata with canned tuna. The fact is that the levels of mercury recorded in the shellfish incriminated in Minamata were from 100 to 1000 times larger than the levels of mercury recorded in the tuna fish.

Significantly, although mercury was found and reported in fish marketed in Canada, Sweden, and England, none of these countries removed fish from the markets, and there was no public hysteria. The joking plaint "What's a mother to do?" became a cry of despair in the United States. Was the mercury incident necessary here? Must the agencies responsible for the health of the Canadians, Swedish, and British be accused of callous disregard for the health of their citizens? Hardly.

In a letter to *The New York Times,* Dr. Leonard J. Goldwater, professor of Community Health Sciences at Duke University, had this to say:

> I would be the last one to deny that there is reason for concern about the presence of mercury compounds (as well

as many other chemicals) in the environment. But I would hope to be among the first to urge that *hasty and ill-considered actions* not be taken merely because there has been a strident outcry from individuals who are poorly informed. (Italics are mine.)

The *Times* of London quoted the Minister of Agriculture of Britain as follows: "Tests have shown that all this fish is within the safety limits set in some other countries, including Sweden, and there is no reason why the housewife should not buy it."

One thing is becoming abundantly clear: our Food and Drug Administration, respected by all countries in the world and looked to by many for guidance, is in the United States becoming everyone's political football to be knocked about for whatever gain may be extracted. I suspect that we will all be losers in this game. But worse, the game is not yet over. We can expect more of the same before some semblance of sanity returns to this troubled arena.

Few people know how or why the Delaney Amendment was enacted or what motivated James J. Delaney, Representative of the Ninth Congressional District of New York, the Borough of Queens, to push for this legislation. Richard M. Stalvey, Managing Editor of *Nutrition Today*, recently took the proverbial bull by its horns and interviewed the father of the controversial "cancer clause" of the food additive law.

According to the Congressman the story is as follows:

One day, for example, it came home forcibly to me as I was drinking hot chocolate. I remembered how in my younger days I made hot chocolate by shaving off thin ribbons of "real" chocolate, which was sold in large bars, and dissolving them in hot milk. When you reached the bottom of the cup there was always a sediment there made up of undissolved chocolate.

Nowadays, chocolate will dissolve even in cold water and there is never a sediment. This means that an emulsifier has been added to the chocolate. I concluded that it must take a very strong chemical to bring about this result. What does such an emulsifier do to the body, I asked myself? What effect does it have on the fat cells in our muscle tissues? I figured that such chemicals must build up residual toxicity in the body. You know, some people can take six or seven drinks without showing any effects, and then with the eighth one they fall down drunk. It was this sort of thing that led me to become seriously interested in the problem.

Thucydides has an Athenian citizen remarking that the two things that interfere most seriously with wise decisions in public affairs are haste and passion. And François, Duc de la Rochefoucauld, wrote: "Great and striking actions which dazzle the eyes are represented by politicians as the effect of great designs, instead of which they are commonly caused by the temper and the passions."

The banning of DDT for crop use by both federal and state agencies is another example of a decision of wide ranging importance having been made in heat and haste by the press and the politicians rather than in a reasonable atmosphere of scientific inquiry. And the battle still goes on, for almost daily the press reports on a number of groups who see DDT as an example of destructive scientific technology and big business' callous disregard for human life.

The scientific reaction to DDT's effects is quite different. The American Chemical Society, a national organization of professional chemists for industry, government, and universities, reported in September, 1969: "The number of illnesses and deaths known to have been caused by accidental or deliberate misuse of pesticides is far outweighed by the benefits these chemicals have brought in controlling disease-bearing pests and in increased production of food. There is no evidence at present that long-term, low-level exposure to pesticides at concentrations approximating those found in the diet or the environment in the U.S. has any deleterious effect on man. At this time, therefore, the net effect of pesticides on human health in the broad sense is positive.*

In December of that year a panel of experts convened by the Secretary of Health, Education, and Welfare issued its report.† The panel noted the total lack of sound evidence implicating DDT as a cause of human illness, given the amounts present in the diet and in the environment. And in June, 1970, Surgeon General Jessie Steinfeld testified before a Congressional committee that he had no evidence that DDT was harmful to human health.

Fed on press reports about the deleterious effects of DDT, the antipesticide forces have ignored these statements and the fact that total diet studies over the past five years have shown harmless levels of pesticide residues in our food.

Actually, on the DDT issue, the public is at war with itself. In one breath consumers condemn the pesticide, and in the next they worry about the imminent starvation of millions as the population explosion continues.** But how are

---

*From "Cleaning Our Environment: The Chemical Basis for Action" prepared by the subcommittee on Environmental Improvement, Committee on Chemistry and Public Affairs, American Chemical Society.
†"Report of the Secretary's Commission on Pesticides and Their Relationship to Environmental Health." It is often referred to as the Mrak report after the chairman of the panel, Emil M. Mrak.
**The Food and Agriculture Organization of the United Nations has recently reported that in 1969 for the first time in 12 years there was no increase in the combined output of the world's farms, fisheries, and forests, while the world's population continued to grow at the annual rate of about 3 percent.

the food growers to increase their yield per available acre without the help of chemical pesticides?

Recently Dr. Hilde Bruch, Professor of Psychiatry at the Baylor College of Medicine, Houston, wrote:

> If early experiences are unwholesome, instead of developing basic trust, an individual will become deeply mistrusting and will experience many situations in life as threatening. Such people become characterologically rigid, repressing many impulses for experiencing satisfaction, and they show an ever-ready tendency to discharge their repressed hostility or project their repressed sexual strivings, whenever a convenient cultural scapegoat is presented to them.
>
> To such individuals, security is equated with purity, and health with naturalness. These are the people who become exceedingly concerned with pure food, pure morals, and pure races. Safety lies in what is old and familiar, and the new and unfamiliar are threatening. New habits, new food, new drugs, or new ideas are all viewed with suspicion and apprehension.*

Technological advances are bound to bring about changes in our lives, and with change comes a certain degree of risk. I do not mean to discredit all the doubts that have been raised over the addition of chemicals to foods, or to suggest that the manufacture, handling, and storage of our food is perfect in every way. The public must face the fact that there are possible, as opposed to actual, hazards associated with the development of an adequate and nourishing food supply for an expanding population. But the public must learn about these hazards from the scientists who are intimately involved in developing this food supply, and not from the nonscientists who intentionally or unintentionally often distort the truth.

---

*"Allure of Food Cults and Nutrition Quackery." *Journal of the American Dietetic Association,* **57** (#4), 316–20, 1970.

In the midst of the prevailing despondency, the public is demanding the impossible—progress without risk. Neither scientists nor the government can guarantee that. But scientists can help by articulating their findings in words that consumers can understand, and the government can help by tightening up the food laws. The present penalties for adulteration of food are far too lenient, and even when a marginal processor is penalized, the judgment against him never receives the wide publicity that would bring him the public condemnation he deserves. It is too easy to avoid the light of public scrutiny. The listing of judgments and legal actions in an obscure journal is no deterrent to marginal operators.

Secondly, I wonder whether the present laws about the listing of ingredients are really in the best interests of the consumer. Obviously that was the aim of Congress when it decreed that all the ingredients of nonstandardized foods and all optional ingredients in standardized foods must be listed on the label. Does benefit from such listing really accrue to the consumer? Can the general consumer extract useful information from the lists, or do they make him queasy and uneasy? If legislators are to legislate, they should know what people want, not what they think they want. To list all ingredients, often resembling a chemical catalog, may be doing more harm than good. And yet, as consumer advocate Betty Furness wrote recently *: "The basic ingredients of French dressing are oil, vinegar, salt, and pepper. So what do we find on the label? Vegetable gum, algin derivative, hydroxypropyl methyl cellulose, with calcium disodium EDTA added as a preservative. You figure they've got to be kidding. Aside from additives that appear to come from ancient Greece,

---

*In *McCall's* magazine, July, 1970.

where are the oil and vinegar and salt and pepper?" She believes that the consumer wants, and the labels should contain, information on the nutritional value of the product: the percentages of fat, carbohydrates, or protein, and the number of calories per 100 grams (3 ounces). However, some semblance of balance is needed here, too. In this regard the recent remark by Virgil Wodica, Director of the FDA's Bureau of Foods seems apt. "What we want is a compromise between a monograph on nutrition and essentially nothing as we now have."

Additionally, for those with special dietary restrictions, including both food idiosyncrasies and religious proscriptions, these, too, could perhaps be noted. A case in point is the difference in ingredients in a can of minestrone soup as made by Campbell and Progresso. Without listing, the bacon in Campbell's version would go unnoticed. And without listing, the egg (protein) in ice cream goes unnoticed, until an allergic hypersensitivity occurs.

As this is a national rather than a local concern, in that all of us would be affected by any legislation proposed or signed into law, I'd suggest that discussion be carried out on both levels before writing your congressman about a personal preference. Consensus would be of greater value to our lawmakers in helping them to formulate a law that we would all have to live with.

Even with the best cooperation between science and government I predict that, before we move out of this period of gloom and doom and before science is rehabilitated, there will be further fiascos on the order of the aminotriazole, cyclamates, and DDT before the public comes to accept the risks associated with the latest innovations in food technology as tranquilly as they do the automobile, the gas stove, the oil furnace, and a hundred other potentially dangerous inventions that we have come to consider essentials.

Perhaps it will be necessary to live through this anti-intellectual antiscience period, with its disregard for evidence in favor of opinion and belief, believing that ultimately people will come to realize that eating an oil-fed steak and an irradiated potato is probably less hazardous than crossing the street.

In this regard it may be well to recall what Thomas Hobbes said three centuries ago: "There is no such thing as perpetual tranquillity of mind while we live here."

On the title page of this book there is a statement by Brillat-Savarin: "The destiny of nations depends upon the manner in which they are fed." I would venture that as a nation we are fed well and will continue to be well fed. I have confidence in our future.

FOLLOW-UP READINGS

Boyland, E., and Goulding, R., *Modern Trends in Toxicology*. London, Butterworth's, 1968.

Chemicals Used in Food Processing. Food Protection Committee, NAS–NRC. Publication #1274, 1965.

Food Chemicals Codex. Food Protection Committee, NAS–NRC. Publication #1406, 1966.

Friedman, Leo, *Safety of Food Additives*. FDA Papers, March, 1970.

Problems in the Evaluation of Carcinogenic Hazard from Use of Food Additives. Food Protection Committee, NAS–NRC. Publication #749, December, 1959.

Procedures for Investigating Intentional and Unintentional Food Additives. World Health Organization, Technical Report Series, #348, Geneva, 1967.

The Safety of Foods: An International Symposium on the Safety and Importance of Foods in the Western Hemisphere. Westport, Conn., Avi Publishing Co., 1963.

Use of Human Subjects in Safety Evaluation of Food Chemicals. Food Protection Committee, NAS–NRC. Publication #1491, 1967.

ACKNOWLEDGMENTS

FIGURES

4. U.S. Department of Agriculture, Agricultural Research Service.

5. *Nutrition Today.*

6. Bowmer, Dr. E. J., "The Challenge of Salmonellosis: Major Public Health Problem." *American Journal of Medical Sciences* (1964), Vol. 247, p. 455.

7. Anita Benarde.

8 and 9. The Fleischmann Laboratories, Standard Brands Incorporated.

10. Sidney Harris in *Medical World News.*

11. Courtesy of Distillation Products Industries.

12 and 21. Food and Drug Administration.

22. Courtesy of Publishers-Hall Syndicate.

23. U.S. Army, Natick Laboratories.

24 and 25. Ralston Purina Company.

26. Courtesy of Alfred Mayor.

27. Reprinted from *Food Technology/Journal of Food Science,* Vol. 24, p. 28 (652). Copyright © 1970 by Institute of Food Technologists.

TABLES

1. Modified from "The Use of Human Subjects in Safety of Food Chemicals." Proceedings of a Conference, National

Academy of Science, Washington, D.C., November 29–30, 1966. Used by permission of P. S. Elias.

2. The Coffee Brewing Center.

4 and 5. The Sugar Association, Inc.

6 and 7. Swaine, Robert, "Natural and Synthetic Flavorings," in Thomas E. Furia, ed., *Handbook of Food Additives.* Chemical Rubber Co., 1968.

10. *Kirk-Othmer Encyclopedia of Chemical Technology,* 2nd ed., Vol. 8. New York, John Wiley & Sons, Inc. Reprinted by permission.

16. "Food and Drug Administration Advisory Committee on Protocols for Safety Evaluations: Panel on Reproduction Report on Reproduction Studies in the Safety Evaluation of Food Additives and Pesticide Residues," in *Toxicology and Applied Pharmacology* (1970), Vol. 16, pp. 264–296.

20. Worthington Foods, Inc.

INDEX

201